A WALK ON THE WILD SIDE

The story of the Wild Bunch and their
20 years study of the flora and fauna
of the Yardley Chase area

1980 – 2000

by

J A RICHARDSON

Purple Emperor

Castle Ashby Trust

CONTENTS

Foreword

Foreword

The Group started in 1980 with the first report issued in 1981 covering mainly the south-west corner of the Chase. In 1984 the Group was requested by the Estate to survey Sane Copse and the surrounding area to further aid discussions with the Nature Conservancy Council (now English Nature) on the conservation management of the SSSI areas within the Chase.

As a result of this request the Group was increased to eight local naturalists covering the main orders of flora and fauna. They have continued to record throughout the Chase and in 1991 extended out to the other Estate woodlands and agricultural land covering some 4,050 hectares.

The main group of recorders, "The Wild Bunch", consisted of Mr Tony Richardson, the late Mr Fred Bennett, the late Mr Peter Gent, Mrs Gill Gent, Mr George Higgs, Mrs Frances Higgs, Mr Colin Wiltshire and Mr David Manning. Other specialist Recorders have been seconded from time to time to cover the lesser studied orders.

The results of all the Group's recording work are published annually; there have been two new national records and 22 new county records. Over 600 plants, 138 mosses, 300+ fungi, 34 butterflies, 790 moths, 20 dragonflies, 150 beetles, 251 flies, 156 spiders, 106 birds, 27 mammals and other groups have been recorded over these past 20 years.

An extensive photo library has been built up over this period and now contains some 6,000 pictures of both flora and fauna including some life cycles together with some of nature's little quirks.

The Wild Bunch Members

Tony Richardson, Entomologist. Born in London in 1927. Moved to Colchester after War Service, working as an Engineer. Co-founder of the Colchester Natural History Society in 1953, main interest then was pond life. Produced a thesis on earwigs and was accepted as a Fellow of the Royal Entomological Society. With others was instrumental in the founding of the Colchester Natural History Museum and was on the Scientific Committee when Fingringhoe Wick Nature Reserve was created. Is a member of the Freshwater Biological Association. Moved to Northampton in 1970 working for Avon Cosmetics and took up natural history photography and stick dressing. Retired in 1986 and has worked with the Compton Estates as advisor on conservation since.

Fred Bennett, Archaeology and Natural History. Born in Ashington, Northumberland 1919-1996. After War Service as an Officer in the Durham Light Infantry became a local authority on Greko/Roman history and travelled to many sites. During his working life in the photographic world, he became interested in natural history. Joined Avon Cosmetics at Sherburn in 1965 and transferred to Avon Northampton in 1976 before retiring in 1984.

Peter Gent, Entomologist. Born in Wellingborough 1916 – 1998. Developed a keen interest in Lepidotera at an early age and carried this throughout the War, collecting specimens abroad on active service in the Middle East and North Africa, After demob, began the study of insects in general and built up a reference collection, also kept bees as well as working for the family firm in Wellingborough. His other interest was in Ancient Egypt and he became a Tutor for Workers Education Association (WEA) and the local authority in both that subject and in insects. Has also contributed to various journals including "Nature of Northamptonshire"

Gill Gent, Botanist. Born in Wellingborough 1927. Developed a keen interest in wild flowers from the age of ten and subsequently became Botanical Recorder for Northamptonshire in the 1960s after bringing up a family. In 1995 wrote and published "The Flora of Northamptonshire and Soke of Peterborough" with Robert Wilson. Has also contributed to "Nature of Northamptonshire" and other publications. Also lectures for the WEA and Leicester University on various botanical subjects.

George Higgs, Lepitopderist. Born in the village of Loughton, Buckinghamshire 1922. From a very early age he began to study the many aspects of natural history in the local countryside. His main interests have always been the study of butterflies, moths and botany. He has studied moths in many parts of the British Isles and since 1967 has run a mercury vapour moth trap in his garden almost on a nightly basis. Since his retirement in 1986 he has travelled to many parts of the world, always with natural history interests in mind. He is a member of the British Entomological and Natural History Society, the Amateur Entomological Society and the Milton Keynes Natural History Society.

Frances Higgs, Bryologist. Began studying Bryophytes in 1987 having been fascinated by them since her childhood in Somerset. Retirement provided time for the detailed work required in the identification of specimens. With her husband, she has travelled widely at home and abroad to enjoy the natural world. Mosses and liverworts have been recorded in many locations and a useful reference collection has been formed. She is a member of the British Bryological Society and the Milton Keynes Natural History Society.

David Manning, Lepidopterist. Born in Bedford 1936. Employed first in civil engineering construction and qualified as a Chartered Quantity Surveyor in 1960. Married to Sylvia in 1962. Worked as a Civil Servant on defence work, first in Kenya and then in Malaya and Scotland. Returned to Bedford in 1968 to work with the Ministry of Transport on the planning and construction of trunk roads and motorways, retiring in 1988. Natural History interests began with birds around 1960 with bird ringing in Malaya and tape recording the largely unknown songs and calls of rain-forest birds. In 1972 started studying British moths, realising that most moth books covered only the larger moths, less than half the British species. The study of the micro moths started by obtaining out-of-print books and new works as they became available. Thirty years later the learning curve continues, helped by meeting and studying with other micro-lepidopterists. Became micro-moth Recorder for Bedfordshire Natural History Society in 1986 and Recorder for Northamptonshire in the 1990s.

Colin Wiltshire, Ornithologist. Born Luton 1937. Boyhood interest in birds was kindled by a fascination with nests and eggs, a common interest in the 1940s. This waned a bit until his angling trips took him back out into the country. Birdwatching being a great diversion when the fish are not biting. As a keen angler, he became more aware of the natural world in general. The pollution of our rivers in the 1960s caused him to become interested in conservation. Due to work and family commitments in the 1970s his angling activities diminished. Missing the birdwatching more than the fishing, he joined the RSPB and went birdwatching at every opportunity and also joined the BTO in 1995. He has developed skills in identifying bird song and other sounds, as often birds can be heard but not seen. Married to Elaine and has twin sons. For 30 years worked in computing on the development of systems on IBM mainframe. For 14 years up to his retirement worked for Reed Book Services at Rushden, initially as a Systems Analyst and for the final 7 years as the Director responsible for computing, retiring early at the age of 57.

Other Recorders

Andy Patmore, FC Ranger.	Deer and Lepidoptera
Ken Blackwell.	Mammals and Reptiles
Colin Read.	Ornithology
Jerry Cooper.	Mycology
Richard Eden.	County Recorder for Dragonflies
Tony White.	County Recorder for Spiders
Douglas Goddard.	Butterfly Conservation Society Recorder

Also grateful thanks for all the help and assistance that has been received from many other groups and individuals. English Nature, Forestry Commission, MoD Conservation, Maurice Goss, Tony Smith, Peter McKay, Lawrence Shelton, George Crawford, Mike Wallace. Dr B S Nau and the close co-operation of the Gamekeepers, Castle Gardeners and the Forest Workers

With special thanks to my daughter Jennifer for her help in the initial preparation of the manuscript.

Introduction

This is the story of the forming and the workings of a dedicated group of naturalists who took on the pleasurable task of studying and recording the varied flora and fauna on the Compton Estate situated at Castle Ashby in Northamptonshire, the centrepiece of this fine Estate for wildlife being the Yardley Chase woodland, situated to the south of the village of Yardley Hastings.

The venture started quite by chance in 1980 when, as a working man, a colleague and I were walking the disused LMS Bedford to Northampton railway track in the Weston Underwood area. This was an activity we had recently taken up as being interesting sites for natural history photography. We gained access to this particular piece of track through the good grace of a local farmer, Mr Maurice Goss, who actively promoted wildlife conservation on his farmland and was maintaining the disused railway track for this purpose. The railway track continued well past Maurice's boundary which ended at the edge of the Chase woodland; we did not then realise the potential of this wooded area we were walking through. Suffice to say that after our morning's walk and returning to our car parked in the farmyard we were anxious to repeat the walk. After a pleasant discussion with Maurice regarding the use of his facilities, this became a regular weekend activity.

Having purchased a large scale map of the area and making some local enquiries we approached the local Forestry Commission (FC), who were managing this woodland, for permission to extend our activities further into the wood. Although the woodland is managed by the FC, they do not own the land. Yardley Chase is a private wood owned by the Marquess of Northampton with private shooting rights; public access is only by prior arrangements.

Permission was granted by the FC for the area of Barnstaple Wood and Ravenstone Road Copse north up to Charcoal Pond. It was in 1983 when, whilst waiting patiently near the pond for dragonflies to pose for me to photograph, a purple emperor butterfly settled on some deer dung on the stone road surface in front of me and proceeded to feed, and it was in range of my lens! It was this photograph that caused me to observe the surrounding area more closely and realise the potential of the site for breeding this very scarce species. It was a typical text book habitat of oaks and sallow. Facing me was an eight feet high chain link fence which was the boundary marker of land used by the Army. I approached the Commanding Officer of the local Simpson Barracks (now demolished) who was in charge of the area and requested permission to gain access to this land. Permission was granted but it wasn't until actually walking the site that I realised it wasn't where I wanted to be and that the Ministry of Defence (MoD) had in fact recently sold back some of their land to Compton Estate; this was where I wanted to be. It should be mentioned here that the land still being used by the Army is in fact owned by the MoD having been purchased during the War. Ecologically it is still part of the Chase and has been included in all our surveys and records.

Whilst retaining my permission to walk the active MoD area, the next step was to enquire from the Estate whether they would allow me to extend my activities further into the Chase and allow me to enter Sane Copse. This area of some 110 hectares recently bought back from the MoD was also a Site of Special Scientific Interest (SSSI). Permission was granted by the Estate who at that time required a comprehensive survey to be carried out to aid discussion with the Nature Conservancy Council (NCC) now English Nature (EN) for future SSSI management. Realising the need for other sciences I gathered together a further group of four dedicated and knowledgeable naturalists to cover other groups of wildlife. This eventually increased the group to eight, including some County Recorders. Between us we amassed 433 years of natural history knowledge and experience. The "Wild Bunch" had arrived.

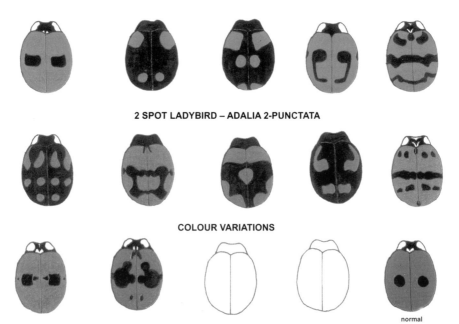

2 SPOT LADYBIRD – ADALIA 2-PUNCTATA

COLOUR VARIATIONS

normal

St Mary Magdalene Church,
foxglove tree in foreground

Terracota Bridge, crossing
Warren Ponds and Park Lake

History of the Estate

COMPTON ESTATE is owned by the Marquess of Northampton and has been in the family prior to 1572 when the present Castle Ashby House was started. The Estate of some 4050 hectares contains some large areas of private ancient woodland, the main area being the Chase consisting of some 703 hectares. The history of the Chase began when Judith, niece of William I (Conqueror), applied to William II (Rufus) to enclose her own hunting area which was granted. The area was enclosed by a fence although little evidence of this can be seen today.

The Chase in those days included Old Pond Close now detached from the main body of woodland at Olney Lane End. The area contained several ponds, some of which still exist whilst others have been filled in and ploughed. The shape of most of these ponds is very irregular consisting of arms and channels, this would appear to indicate they were man-made or at least shaped by man for a purpose. The arms would have been very useful for fish husbandry as a food source. Those ponds that can still be found within the existing woodland area are mostly silted up and overgrown. The two Deer Park ponds still contain good water as do Denton Wood and Biggin Lodge, the latter being the remains of a moat that used to surround the lodge. Two new largish ponds have been dug by the shoot for the purpose of duck releases, one in Denton Wood and one in the Deer Park, and also the enlargement of the north Deer Park pond. Unfortunately these will not be very productive for general flora and fauna as large numbers of ducks only produce a green pea soup environment, also large quantities of corn in the water will severely de-oxygenate the pond.

Two of these old ponds have been cleared out by the FC and the Wild Bunch Group. Charcoal Pond alongside the stone road in Ravenstone Road Copse was dredged and dammed at one end to increase the water depth. The encroaching scrub was cleared and it is now a good pond with an increase in pond life. The other pond situated on a ride edge in the SW corner of Ravenstone Road Copse was extremely choked up and overgrown and although shown on the map it did not have a name so, for ease of reference, we christened it Star Pond due to its shape. We cleared this pond because it was the only one in the vicinity of a large, recently opened out ditch in which we found the Palmate Newt – *Triturus helveticus* and the work was done to hopefully increase its breeding habitat.

There are other smaller woods on the eastern side of the Estate, Long Furlong, Cold Oak Copse and Horn Wood together totalling some 118 hectares. The ordnance survey map of the area printed in 1835 shows that Long Furlong and Cold Oak Copse were in fact one wood. The map was issued some 20 – 30 years after being drawn, and by then the wood had already been separated by the first Marquess; probably due to the national need for timber and cereals during the Napoleonic Wars.

Other fragmental pockets of coppice and woodland are scattered throughout. The Firs and Whiston Spinney to the north, Engine and Paradise Ponds area and the woodland surrounding the Castle. There is also an old brickyard with its worked-out hollows and pits. The main pit is now a large pond but it is rather dark and very overhung with vegetation. The Estate started making bricks and tiles on this site in the late 1800s to enable good quality housing to be built in Castle Ashby village. It has produced its own unique design of ridge tile not found elsewhere. It also produced land drainage pipes for use on the Estate. The pit ceased working in 1930 and the one kiln is still standing although it is now rather dilapidated. This little area has produced some interesting botanical species and in the small spinney at the top of the hill is a memorial to the 6th Marquess.

The Castle gardens, designed by Capability Brown in 1761, are bordered by semi-wild ground and arboretum with the main Park and Menagerie Ponds and the northerly Scotland and Grendon Quarter Ponds. There are some terrapins on Grendon Quarter Pond which have survived there for several years. These surrounding grounds have retained some very interesting and scarce plants as well as two ice houses and a lime kiln and of course a ha-ha to protect the formal gardens, all of these being good wildlife habitats.

Park Pond was drained in 1997 to enable it to be restocked with fish. We took advantage of this lengthy period of dryness to check the base with metal detectors. It was an interesting exercise although no hidden family treasure was found. The main part of the discoveries was four pieces of silver jewellery, 125 coins (the oldest dated 1874), 14 rounds of WWII ammunition (used and unused) including two German parachute flare cases printed "use by 31.5.1944", lots of angling debris, spoons, lures and weights and a couple of bucketfuls of other metal waste. Unfortunately this prolonged period of dryness caused the loss of our only colony of a Nerite water snail – *Theodoxus fluviatillis*. Because of its preference for a stony-based wave-lapped habitat it is a very scarce snail in Northamptonshire.

The 14th-15th century Castle Church, dedicated to St Mary Magdalene, contains a good colony of pipistrelle bats over the porch and the churchyard has some interesting plants, White Butterbur- *Petasites albus* and winter Heliotrope – *P.fragrans*, together with a Foxglove Tree – *Paulownia tomentosa* planted in the mid 1930s by the 6th Marquess. This very attractive flowering tree is a native of China and has an irregular flowering pattern as it is affected by our winter climate. The churchyard also has a gothic cross, 6m high, in memory of the 3rd Marquess, while in a recess an angel watches over the grave of the 4th Marchioness.

Hundreds of years ago the whole of south-east Northamptonshire was covered with woodland, timber in those days being probably more important than today as apart from heavily timbered houses our Navy consisted of wooden ships (2000 oaks = 50 acres = 1 warship). What we have left today are the relics of this vast wood, the big ones being Salcey Forest, Yardley Chase and Hazelborough. Yardley Chase is situated in the ancient Hundred of Wymersley mentioned in the Doomsday Book, the name Wymersley appears on the board at the entrance to the local FC office in Denton Wood. There were mainly two types of woodland recognised in those days, Crown Woods owned by the Crown with very severe penalties for wrong-doings (Salcey) and Chases where the rights of hunting were granted by the King to some worthy person (Yardley). We have to thank our Norman ancestors and their successors for their interest in deer for venison and hunting. Had the deer and the woods not been protected by these strict laws many more of our ancient forests would have been cleared and lost forever.

The next major changes came with the Yardley Hastings Enclosure Act of 1776 which affected the grazing rights of the commoners. Coppicing, in those days, was well practised with the underwood being cut at regular intervals and the stands of oak and ash were left to form mature timber, good quality oak being used for planks and beams with poorer quality being used for posts etc. The bark of oak was taken for tanning for the local leather industry and charcoal was made from the branch wood for use in local forges and as household fuel. One of the old ponds on the edge of Ravenstone Road Copse is named Charcoal Pond. Apart from the value of the timber, game management was also practised and by the end of the 19th century the woods were grown mainly for sport rather than timber profit.

In 1929 the decision was made to grant a 999 year lease to the recently established FC; this became active in 1931 with the Estate retaining all the sporting rights.

By the late 1930s the woods were cleared mainly of all the oak, ash and poplar which were required for the War effort and replanting with fast growing soft woods was started. The MoD at that time took over a part of the Chase woodland (Sane Copse and part of Denton Wood and the Deer Park) for use as a storage area for explosives. These two areas had been replanted by the FC but were then neglected and the current timber crop of these areas seems to be natural regeneration apart from the conifer blocks.

Up to the late 1960s and early 1970s the general timber crop varied from soft wood to hard wood depending on the current trend at the time. This caused the removal and killing of large quantities of young oak to make way for fast growing conifers. This amount of diversity has had some detrimental effects on the ancient wood eco-system. After the early 1970s, due to public and media pressure, the public were demanding a more conservation orientated type of management policy because of the increasing awareness of its ancient woodland status.

At this time the NCC had declared a part of Ravenstone Road Copse and the MoD land to be a SSSI which imposed certain restrictions on the type of management that could be practised.

The dry mid-1990s severely affected the shallow rooted conifers causing them to be prematurely cropped allowing these areas to be replanted with hardwoods, an encouraging move from the conservation point of view.

With the original clear fell exercise of the early 1930s the bush grass – *Calamagrostis epigejos* became rife throughout the woodland area. This very invasive grass is unpalatable to most grazing animals but it will be eaten by cattle in the absence of better fodder. The introduction of the Local Enclosure Act severely affected the amount of grazing done by the commoners' cattle which allowed this grass to become well established but controlled under a thick wood canopy. However, once timber is felled letting in light, the grass surges upwards, smothering any normal woodland flora vegetation. This prevents any coppicing that is carried out today from giving us the habitat that we would hope to get.

At the start of WWII, due to its close proximity to a main line railway, a large part of the Chase was taken over by the MoD for the construction of bunkers to store explosives. These covered approximately 300 hectares where 44 surface bunkers were built together with a small barracks on the west boundary which were contained within a 7½ mile long perimeter security fence. Fifteen miles of railway track were laid, together with drainage, connecting them all with the LMS railway running along the south boundary of the Estate and connecting at Horton Station. The last main line trains, Bedford to Northampton, ran in the mid-1960s. The bunkers were closed down in the late 1970s and the railtrack was removed for use in India. A part of the site (Sane Copse) was sold back to the Estate in 1983. The remainder is still a secure area and used by the Army as a training ground.

With the building of the bunkers the army created an exceptionally good wildlife area. The brick bunkers had to have the protection of a blast wall around them and these were created by digging out the surrounding heavy clay ground and using the spoil to build these high earthworks. This operation left large clay pits which soon filled with rainwater and ditch drainage. They were at that time all connected by underground land drainpipes to prevent flooding and eventual run-off into ditches. These ponds were maintained by the army as a fire fighting source but it wasn't long before other things took an interest in them and now, after 50 plus years, they are providing a rich source of flora and fauna. During the war years the site was managed quite differently to the present time. In those days all bunker earthworks and surrounding land were close mown and large areas of meadow were regularly ploughed each year because of the annual large crop of white ox-eye daisy which caused the bunkers to be clearly visible to any enemy aircraft. Since then scrub and thorn have rapidly encroached giving us the habitat we have today. There are over 120 ponds of varying sizes ranging in depth from 1-4 metres and they have provided us with one of the largest local populations of the Great Crested Newt – *Triturus cristatus* and 20 of the 45 species of British dragonflies and are all rich in plant life.

In the early 1970s the NCC had declared part of the Chase and all of the MoD land to be a SSSI. The site was re-appraised in 1982 just before the re-purchase of Sane Copse from the MoD. The declaration of a SSSI does put certain restrictions on the management of the affected woodland. A management plan has to be drawn up and agreed by all parties to prevent undue disturbance of the local flora and fauna whilst the woodland is commercially worked. This SSSI area covers approximately half of Ravenstone Road Copse and all Sane Copse as well as the still active MoD area on the west side (Colliers Hern, Northampton Copse, Bunchgrass Copse and Shortgrove Copse).

These areas were re-surveyed by English Nature in 1980-1981 and were found to contain some nationally scarce butterflies, as well as the great crested newts, and still retained ancient woodland indicator species of plants. These selected woods and meadows are now being sympathetically managed to conserve the wildlife habitats. This is being achieved by close liaison between the Estate, FC, MoD and EN strongly supported by the 'Wild Bunch' and the information and records submitted by them annually.

Woodland

The woodland is the most fruitful part of the Estate providing a rich variety of habitats, mostly stocked with FC plantings, the average age of which would be 60 years. The Deer Park and some ride edges still contain old original oak, lime and hornbeam. The woodland floor is mainly clay and is very wet, and in the 1980s there were very few days of the year when it wasn't necessary to wear wellies. Since then it has improved some due to recent ditching and drainage programme together with the dry mid 1990s but it doesn't take much rain to bring the rides back to welly wearing conditions.

Because of the large area covered by woodland we decided to split them all into sections for recording purposes. The original Chase records are covered in the first six sections, later extended to nine, to cover the other eastern woods. The sections now number up to twelve to cover other major habitats, the Castle grounds, disused sandpit and disused ironstone quarry and spinney. Details of the boundaries of the sections, together with map references, can be found on page 66. Species found elsewhere on the Estate, mainly arable land, are not recorded in the detailed lists at the rear of this book unless it is a noteworthy species when it will be recorded separately.

The first two or three years kept us all very busy with some of us almost living in the woods. Everything that we saw and could identify was written down and logged in its respective section. It took some time before we were fully orientated so that we knew where all the odd little nooks and crannies were located and were able to walk directly to them by cutting through the woods in an (almost) straight line. A lot of walking and scrambling was done with quite a few base over apex experiences, there were numerous night operations, running the moth light at as many locations as we could manage, all these night operations being greatly dependent on the weather. In 1990 the Estate gave us the use of a small old Army building, affectionately referred to as 'The Lodge', which has enabled us to store some equipment and tools and eventually our small dinghy. It is also very handy on a cold winter's day to have a brew-up in reasonable comfort.

It is always the greenery that seems to attract people to the countryside so where better to start than in the woods to discuss the various plants that can be found there. To get a really good feeling for the habitat it is necessary to get off the beaten track and into the thick stuff. Certainly all the rides and tracks must be walked through at all seasons as this is where the majority of our flowering species are to be found but it is surprising what extras can be found by getting out the machette and pushing through into the middle. One should always carry a stout stick for getting at overhanging branches and for bramble and nettle bashing.

Apart from the FC plantings of conifers the main trees are oak, ash, poplar and hazel with a good covering of underwood species and these are all affected by the weather.

English weather, as we all know, is very variable and we should all be well used to it by now. We seem to have lost our seasons and just have weather.

The very hot, dry years of 1989-1990 had a noticeable effect on the woodland flora and caused the pond levels to drop severely, a drop of 50cm, and some of the shallower ponds to dry up completely. It was due to these conditions that we decided to measure the rain and pond levels by purchasing a rain gauge and installing depth marker posts in some of the ponds.

The weather over these past years has been very unseasonal with the rain coming at all the wrong times coupled with some very hot periods. 1995-1996 were two more such dry years causing some springs to cease flowing and again causing some ponds to dry up completely. The spring in the Deer Park, which has reputedly never stopped flowing, did stop in1995 and has not yet started to flow again. This caused the northern Deer Park pond to completely dry up and produced cracks in the pond bottom to a depth of 36cm, the cracks in the surrounding woodland were up to 46cm deep, this pond now has to rely on run off from the surrounding grassland for its supply of water.

The larger trees did suffer during these drought conditions in that their wood became dry and brittle so that any light wind caused some branches to break easily and some of the old park trees lost quite a bit of timber. Another cause of timber damage in 1995 was the fall of very wet snow (8cm) in March. The weight of this snow, which settled thickly on these brittle branches caused many of them to snap off and overhung trees to fall, especially on ride edges. There were more trees and branches broken through this snow than in the previous year's high winds.

As a general rule ponds remain full from October to April and then, as the trees green up, the levels start to drop by about 15 – 20cm this being the normal seasonal tree uptake. It is the temperature and rainfall which then causes any extra drop in the levels. The maximum drop usually occurs between July and September. These heavy drops in the levels do not greatly affect the fauna in the larger/deeper ponds but the smaller/shallower ponds can dry up completely and remain so for three to four months. This does affect the larger species such as newts and dragonflies. The newts may only lose one generation (eggs and tadpoles) but dragonflies have up to a three year cycle. It will of course also affect any species that have their larval stages in water such as beetles and flies, although the pupal stage will mostly survive in mud and some eggs can cope with dehydration.

In spite of the emphasis made on the prolonged dry periods over these past years there have also been periods of very heavy rain, often at the wrong time. This has caused severe flooding in some

ANNUAL RAINFALL & POND LEVELS

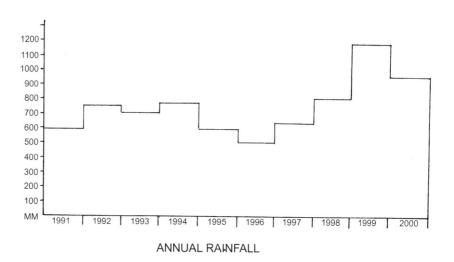

ANNUAL RAINFALL

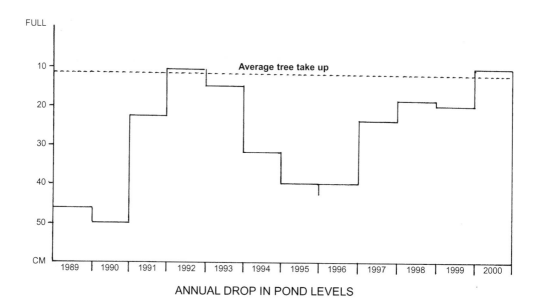

ANNUAL DROP IN POND LEVELS

parts of the country but not, I'm glad to say, on our patch. We have been left with some very waterlogged areas which, apart from affecting the farming activities, had very detrimental effects on wild-life. Any overwintering larvae or pupa and even some adult insects will die if submerged in water for a long period. This will affect population numbers of insects in the following spring. This is the time when they should be coming out of hibernation to continue their cycle. Shortage of insect food at fledgling time can seriously affect small birds. But, getting back to the trees –

There are still some 200-250 year old oaks in the Deer Park and on the edge of some rides and avenues. The majority, however, are the FC plantings and are around 60 years old. Those in the Deer Park and similar areas are now showing signs of wear and tear and losing the odd limb or two and this is where fungus can start to attack. It is important, where trees of this age occur, to start a re-planting plan early and this is what is happening in the Estate park. For many years now young oaks have been planted in cages to protect them from browsing and these have been carefully sited so as not to spoil the overall panorama in years to come. Oaks are the best tree for providing support for insect life. It is listed as supporting 284 species which feed either directly on it or are specifically parasitic on those which do. Apart from its insect population which makes it a very popular tree among small birds, an old tree may have as many as 30 or more different species of lichen growing on its bark and a large array of fungi can live on its dead or decaying wood. In its lifetime a tree can produce millions of acorns of which very few will survive as trees. They are avidly sort after by rodents and deer and many are carried off by pigeons and jays. Even in winter you can still see small birds searching the bark and twigs for insect eggs and pupa. As branches fall and hollows develop they become roosting places for owls and bats and various wood boring beetles will take over, some spending many years in the larval stage. Some of the very old specimens, especially if left in isolation on a lawn or from clearing and ploughing, could be declared a SSSI in their own right. Any fallen branches from those oaks should be left lying unless they constitute a hazard. I would apply this doctrine to other fallen trees or branches, we are inclined to be much too tidy with our woodlands and this debris is a good habitat for something smaller. Our main species on the Estate are the Common – *Quercus robur, Q. pedunculate*, Sessile – *Q. petraea*, a scattering of Turkey Oak – *Q.cerris* and in the gardens are Holme Oak – *Q. ilex*. Turkey oak is a Mediterranean species which has been widely planted and is now naturalised in southern England. Its timber is of no commercial value. Oaks generally are good trees to beat for insect life. Beating is where you stand under a branch with the tray in one hand (a frame covered in white cloth) and a long stick in the other, give the branch a good whack with the stick and examine the various forms of life that fall into the tray. This is where you need a sharp pair of eyes and have to be very deft with your plastic specimen boxes. Having examined the contents of the tray always remember to empty the tray wherever possible over a suitable branch of the same species of tree, disregarding anything that has gone down your neck!

Moving on through the woods, probably the next most prolific tree is the self regenerated Silver Birch – *Betula pendula,* and the not so frequently seen Downy Birch – *B.pubescens* is scattered about in some sections. Birch regenerates very easily and can reach almost weed proportions, its seed being very light and small and is wind blown some considerable distance. It is not fussy about its soil and will take root almost anywhere i.e. cracks in brickwork, gutters etc. Its life expectancy is about 60 years. Birch does not have a great commercial value other than pea sticks and besom brooms. The tops of saplings are often used in the construction of jumping fences in equestrian events.

Ash – *Fraxinus excelsior* a native tree and is an important timber producer. Its light coloured wood, being very strong and hardwearing, is used a lot in the furniture industry. It also makes good walking sticks when young and is sometimes grown just as a commercial crop for sticks and shepherds crooks.

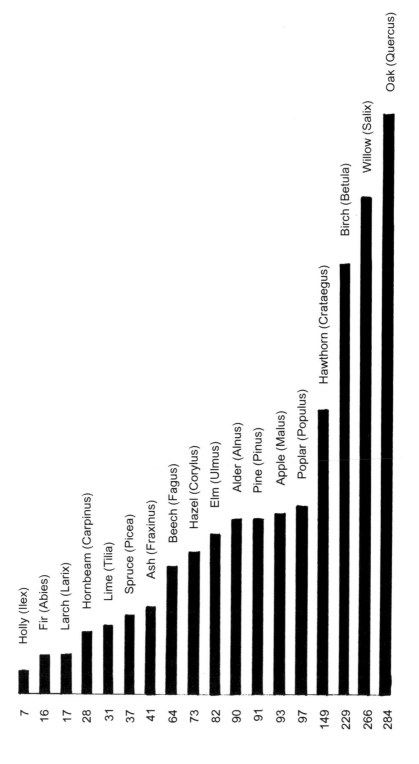

INSECTS ASSOCIATED WITH FOREST TREES

Tree	Number
Holly (Ilex)	7
Fir (Abies)	16
Larch (Larix)	17
Hornbeam (Carpinus)	28
Lime (Tilia)	31
Spruce (Picea)	37
Ash (Fraxinus)	41
Beech (Fagus)	64
Hazel (Corylus)	73
Elm (Ulmus)	82
Alder (Alnus)	90
Pine (Pinus)	91
Apple (Malus)	93
Poplar (Populus)	97
Hawthorn (Crataegus)	149
Birch (Betula)	229
Willow (Salix)	266
Oak (Quercus)	284

Many woodland trees and shrubs support large numbers of insects which feed either directly on some part of the plant or are specifically parasitic on those which do.

Hazel – *Corylus avellana* is our main understorey growth and was the main coppicing material of years gone by, an industry that is now declining. Coppicing was the mainstay for the survival of the ancient forests, being cut every 7 to 9 years. This gave us the rotation of habitats necessary to provide a varied, rich and diverse wildlife content, something that is lacking in a lot of our woods today. The crop of poles was used mainly for sheep hurdles and in hedge laying, the requirement for both of these is almost nil these days although I am pleased to see that the practice of hedge laying is now being encouraged over the past few years by some councils.

Some of the hedges on the Estate are now being laid and are worth seeing as they are a necessary revival of old skills. Anything that is done to encourage good strong hedge growth is essential for these modern days where the tendency now is to treat hedges with disrespect. The loss of any hedge is a severe blow to the continuation of species as apart from destroying a habitat, as such, it is removing an essential connecting corridor between habitat areas. This is one of the main reasons for the loss of some of our species. With the fragmentation of our woodlands these days it is essential that these corridors remain.

Nuts would also have been a good crop well worth harvesting but these days you have to be very quick to beat the grey squirrel, an alien species introduced to this country in the late 1800s. He has an uncanny knack of knowing just when the kernel has formed and immediately takes it. Although most of his gatherings are buried they are often not ripe enough to produce seedlings and this can have a severe effect on the regeneration of this tree.

The hazel is probably the earliest flower of the spring. The male catkins formed in the autumn are often open in January but I feel that spring has really arrived when the female catkin can be found which appears as a small bud-like structure with dark red filaments protruding from its tip.

Poplars these days consist of many hybrid varieties planted as a commercial crop. Most common is the hybrid Black – *Populus x canadensis* which is usually seen in blocks or rows and is grown mainly for pulping. Denton Wood does have some Balsam Poplar – *P. balsamifera*, an introduction from the Americas of some 300 years ago but is now nationally a very scarce tree. These trees were planted at the head of some rides at the centre of Chestnut Star. There were eight of them but now only four remain, the others having been inadvertently felled when the new forest road was laid in 1993, these are the only ones recorded on the Estate.

Grey Poplar – *P. canescens* has only been recorded in three sections. This is a more vigorous tree and can reach a height of 30 metres. This tree is the food plant of a very scarce micro moth – *Ectoedemia turbidella* which feeds in a leaf mine on the leaves of a mature tree. This moth was recorded in 1996 and was a new record for the county and the 30th nationally.

To our knowledge there are now no confirmed sightings of the Black Poplar - *P. nigra* being found on the Estate.

There is a good old avenue of Horse Chestnut (Conker) – *Aesculus hippocastanum* in Olney Lane End. This tree was introduced to the country around 1605-1617. The fruits, conkers, grow easily which often accounts for the odd tree cropping up here and there, children and adults collect them for the game of 'Conqueror' which gets them well dispersed.

The fruit is a favourite of deer and in the autumn you can guarantee to see several fallow and some muntjac deer under the canopy of this avenue. Our most famous conker tree is the 'Family Tree' situated in the grounds of the Castle. It is over 200 years old and because the branches have not been browsed they have drooped to the ground and rooted at the tips forming a complete ring of trees around the parent trunk. Indeed, the branches from these have also struck starting another ring except where they have overstretched the ha-ha and become browsed by cattle. These rings are still all directly connected with the parent tree and now cover an area of some 1200 square metres.

There are also scattered about the red flowered species – *A. x carnea* which produces its fruit with mainly unspiked cases.

Lime trees are scattered throughout the woods mainly on ride edges, both the Common – *Tilia x vulgaris* and the Small Leaved - *T.cordata*. There is a very good avenue of old specimens of the common in Denton Wood showing the dense clusters of suckers that form around the base of the trunks. The small leaved is very sparse on the Estate and has only been recorded in three sections.

As we all know it is not a good policy to park one's car, even for a short time, beneath these trees because of the excessive aphid honeydew continually falling from the leaves, and certainly not an open top model!

Because of our very wet habitat and the large number of ponds situated in the woods we have quite a lot of Alder – *Alnus glutinosa*. This is a tree that likes to have its roots bathed in water and some large thickets have developed around most of the ponds especially where the pond edge scrub has been cleared and the stumps have regenerated. The buds in spring have a noticeable blue hue to them and the male catkins become very colourful as they open up. In their right habitat, near water, they are very prolific and the numerous seeds released from the cones are scattered on to the water. These seeds contain two minute air sacs which enables them to stay afloat for some time and be moved about by the wind. The female cones left on the tree through the winter leave you in no doubt as to what tree it is, even from a distance. Charcoal produced from alder is considered the best quality for gunpowder.

Our wet habitat also provides us with plenty of willow and sallow. Probably one of the most noticeable and welcome sights in the spring is the Pussy Willow – *Salix caprea*, also known as Goat Willow or Great Sallow, with its furry silver male catkins soon turning yellow with pollen which is eagerly sought after by bees, butterflies and moths.

The Purple Willow – *S. purpurea*, first mentioned as being in the Chase by G C Druce, has been recorded but only on one pond. This is a tree easily overlooked and our search for another specimen has been unfruitful. This one was nearly lost to us as it was only discovered about two days before it would have been felled in a scrub clearance operation.

When the Estate bought back Sane Copse and its many ponds from the MoD the scrub growth around these bunker ponds had become a serious problem. The pond edge scrub was meeting up with the scrub now growing on the bunker earthworks making some of these areas almost impenetrable. A ten year plan of clearance was agreed with English Nature and work commenced in 1992. The inside edges of the ponds were completely cleared but leaving any mature trees, mainly birch and willow, at intervals of about 30 metres. The banks of the earthworks were considered too steep to be safely managed so they still have a good coverage of scrub thorn, rose and the odd ash and birch. The outside edge of the pond was cleared back to the encroaching woodland to a depth of 5 – 6 metres and in a scalloped pattern, again leaving some mature trees. Charlie and Richard, the woodsmen, were very good at spotting various insects and birds and were well aware of the wildlife going on around them, sometimes presenting us with a matchbox containing a grub or insect and keeping us up to date on the wildlife activities in their area.

The rest of the understorey is very varied with plenty of hawthorn, both common and midland, the latter is the one with two seeds in the fruit. Blackthorn provides a good crop of sloes, very useful for making sloe gin. There is also Purging Buckthorn – *Rhamnus catharticus* scattered about, some of which have developed into good sized trees. This and the Alder Buckthorn – *Frangula alnus* is the larval foodplant of the brimstone butterfly, the alder buckthorn however has not recorded on the Estate. The lush clumps of black berries can look appetising but with the name 'catharticus' woe-betide anyone who eats them. Guelder rose and wayfaring tree are plentiful along the ride edges producing rosettes of white flowers which later give a good showing of red and black berries in the autumn. We have recorded one bush of a yellow berried guelder rose – *Viburnum sargentii v. flavum*. Privet – *Lingustrum vulgare* abounds in all sections producing good nectar bearing flowers and a plentiful supply of berries in the autumn.

Honeysuckle – *Lonicera periclymenum* can be found climbing and trailing amongst the trees, the white to yellow flowers producing quite a heady fragrance on warm evenings. They are a nectar source for moths, the corolla tube being generally too long for other nectar seeking insects. Unlike ivy, this shrub does cause damage to growing trees, making them unmarketable apart from firewood. It twines itself, always in a left to right movement, around the trunk or branch usually starting with young saplings and as the support grows and expands the honeysuckle does not give, becoming tighter until the tree will gradually grow over the honeysuckle stem sometimes burying it completely. This deforms the tree into interesting twisted shapes which do make good walking sticks (did I not say that I also make walking sticks!)). This shrub is the larval foodplant of the uncommon white admiral butterfly and the sticky red fruits are much sought after by blackbirds.

Spindle – *Eunonymus europaeus* is a native shrub which is scattered throughout the Estate woodlands and hedges. It is quite inconspicuous in the spring and summer, with its small white flowers, but the autumn shows it in its full beauty. The four-celled fruits ripen in September to give a striking show of bright rosy-pink. When fully ripe they open to expose four brilliant orange-coloured seeds. They are very poisonous but much liked by blackbirds and thrushes, in spite of this they often remain long after other fruits have been taken. The wood is hard and fine grained and was much in demand for making spindles and skewers.

Ivy – *Hedera helix* is a good strong climber and can be seen anywhere in the countryside climbing walls and trees and, in the absence of these, running thickly over the ground. The berries are avidly devoured by blackbirds and others, the indigestible seed eventually being passed out to take root wherever it falls. The umbels of the late autumnal flowers are probably the last source of nectar for any late flying bees, flies and wasps and it is not unusual on a sunny day to see a late flying butterfly join in the feeding session. Ivy is a free-growing plant with its own trunk which can reach a diameter of 30cm but it does need support and can sometimes completely cover a tree or a wall. It is not parasitic on the tree in any way and unlike honeysuckle does no damage as it will expand with the supporting tree, the only damage caused would be just the weight of the covering ivy causing dying branches to snap off. It is an excellent roosting place for insects and small birds in the winter.

The grounds around the Castle, apart from the arboretum, have many other interesting species of trees not found naturally in local woodland. One that is worthy of mention is the Weeping Beech – *Fagus v. pendula* planted in the late 1700s. It has had to be chained at the top to prevent the branches splitting the trunk but even with this precaution it did lose a large branch in 1998 due to high winds which luckily has not noticeably changed its overall shape. There is another smaller tree growing on the lawn by the Orangery.

Fowering plants

Moving on now to the flowering plants, I have to say that although the majority of our recordings were made in the first ten years, we had not found them all. In 1996 it was felt that there would not be many more new records so a small flora was issued but since then we have added 31 more species, two of which were added this year (2000). It has to be said that unless you stand on this particular piece of ground at this time of the year you won't see this particular plant. If there had not been so many pairs of knowledgeable eyes searching over the ground so many times we would probably have missed a good number of our listed species.

It is important and more than half the fun, to get off the rides and beaten tracks and push into the thick stuff. So many of the plants that were plentiful 150 years ago have now, due to the severe afforestation changes, reduced greatly in number. Whilst they are mostly still with us they are reduced to quantities of a dozen or so or even in some cases to one or two specimens.

Orchids especially have suffered in this way and it took us 14 years (1994) to find our only specimen of the Birds-nest Orchid – *Neottia nidus-avis* which does not appear on any accessible records but was mentioned as being in the Chase in Druce's 1930 Flora of Northamptonshire. Our most common orchid is the Common Spotted – *Dactylorhiza fuchsii* being found on most of our rides. The other orchid species are very scarce indeed. The Early Purple – *Orchis mascula*, previously plentiful, is now only sparsely scattered through the Chase although it has started to increase over the past four to five years. The Bee Orchid – *Ophrys apifera* is now only found on one very small patch of grassland near a bunker in Sane Copse. In 1990 the Violet Helleborine – *Epipactis purpurata* was found in just three locations. They were wired off to prevent the deer from browsing them but were only seen again in 1992 and not since. Our woodland area is thought to be the extreme of this plant's northern range, maybe one of these days we will see it again.

I think that one of the best sights of early spring on the Estate are the carpets of Winter Aconite – *Eranthis hyemalis*, these can be seen in the gardens and surrounding area and alongside Engine Pond. This plant was introduced to the grounds of large houses in the 1700s and has now become naturalised in a few places in southern England. Nationally it is a very scarce plant and we are very fortunate to have the quantity that we do. To see them at their best you do need to pick a sunny day. With a bit of diligent searching towards the end of the snowdrop period you can find a few clumps of Spring Snowflake – *Leucojum vernum* in the surrounding woodland.

Abraham-Isaac-Jacob – *Trachystemon orientalis* can also be found from late March. This plant was introduced from east Bulgaria in the 1750s and is now established in a few areas of southern England and only recorded in Northamptonshire at Castle Ashby. The Wild Tulip – *Tulipa sylvestris* can also be found. This is probably a native of France and is now naturalised in woods and orchards in very scattered localities mainly in central and south-east England. There are only two or three known locations for this plant in Northamptonshire.

Yellow Figwort – *Scrophularia vernalis* can be found in the wilder parts of the gardens and is only recorded from two other sites in Northamptonshire. It was first recorded by G Adams in 1892. Greater Spearwort – *Ranunculus lingua* can be found growing in Warren Ponds in the park grounds, it is only known at one other locality near Peterborough.

Lesser Periwinkle – *Vinca minor* which occurs in only one small area of woodland gives us a splash of blue colour from March to May and it sometimes produces a white sport. It is an occasional perennial found locally in woods and hedgebanks.

One plant that has been lost to us is the Star of Bethlehem – *Ornithogalum umbellatum* a rare native bulb that used to grow on the north bank of Scotland Pond. This disappeared when the ponds were dredged in 1991 to improve the fishing conditions.

Monkshood – *Aconitum napellus* can be found growing on the south-east bank of Park Pond by the terracotta bridge. This is a native perennial growing in damp places, mainly in south-west England. It gives us deep blue flowers in June to September, the whole plant is very poisonous as it contains the alkaloid Aconitine.

Mentioning Engine Pond earlier, this is the site of our Blue-eyed Mary – *Omphalodes verna* which flowers from March to May. This small blue flower is an introduced perennial now locally naturalised in some parts of southern England and is the only site in Northamptonshire. This plant was nearly lost to us in the early 1990s due to the Euro legislated requirement to construct flood/overflow plains in the vicinity of large areas of water. Fortunately one or two plants did manage to survive and were carefully watched, and I am pleased to say that they have now successfully re-colonised the area.

Back in the main woodlands the year usually starts its flowering season with a flash of yellow along some stone road edges of Coltsfoot – *Tussilago farfara*, the flowers of which can appear as early as March. This is a very common native perennial producing its leaves after flowering and was used for medicinal work in the treatment of coughs.

This plant is closely followed by the Primrose – *Primula vulgaris* and the Wood Anemone – *Anemone nemorosa*. We do have a good number of primroses, including a large clump of the double form, which was of course photographed. Wood Anemones, unfortunately, are extremely scarce giving us just a glimpse of delicate white in April and May. It used to be plentiful producing large sweeps in many parts of the woods but it is now restricted to only two sites both on the south-east side of the Estate, one of a few scattered plants and the other an area of about ten square metres. This plant has suffered greatly from the changes in woodland management. It does occur in places in the Castle grounds and a very nice double form was found and photographed in 1997. Lesser Celandine – *Ranunculus ficaria* gives us large patches of bright yellow with the Blackthorn – *Prunus spinosa* turning the hedges quite white. This hedgerow shrub is the larval foodplant of the very rare black hairstreak butterfly.

Druce recorded the Stinking Hellebore – *Helleborus foetidus* as being present in the Chase but it had not been recorded since. In 1990 in the MoD section it was rediscovered when the remnants of an old dilapidated hedge line was grubbed out to erect a wire cattle fence. In the disturbed ground along the top of the ditch about a dozen seedlings were found growing. These were found dislodged a few weeks later, probably by some small browsing animal. The area was then wired round and two of the plants did reach maturity and one flowered. These two plants soon died off and no further seedlings have been found, probably because there was no further disturbance of the ground coupled with the encroachment of coarse grasses.

Cowslips – *Primula veris* are sparsely scattered in some rides and meadows and where they grow in close proximity to primroses they can hybridise and produce the False Oxlip – *P. vulgaris x veris* which is not a common plant although it is found in many places on the Estate.

Although there are plenty of Bluebells – *Endymion non-scriptus* throughout the woods we have only one carpeted area and that is House Wood in the MoD area. These plants often produce white sports and some pink and we have got one patch of the long bracted variety – *var. bracteosa*. As the bluebells get towards the end of their flowering period you should start to see the early purple orchid on flower. This plant is now very scarce on the Estate. A little later Herb Paris – *Paris quadrifolia* should appear. This is an ancient wood indicator species and is very scarce in the county. Patches of this plant have been discovered from time to time during wood clearance operations and these patches are always marked with a stake and where possible the site is managed to assist its continued flowering.

The Arum – *Arum maculatum* widely known as Lords and Ladies is a very prolific plant and over the past few years seems to be increasing. Normally the flower has a brown spadix but sometimes it is cream coloured. It has the smell of rotting meat and attracts small flies which get trapped in the base of the spathe (hood) and, in their attempts to escape, dislodge male pollen and pollinate the female ovaries, if lucky the fly escapes. This plant has accumulated a host of local names nationally, all having phallic associations. Some local Northamptonshire names being Bobbin and Joan, Bulls and Cows, Cows and Calves, Cuckoo Flower, Cuckoo Pintle, Dog Bobbins, Ladies and Gentlemen, Lambs-lekens.

Bugle – *Ajuga reptans* is a common plant and spreads rapidly by runners. It gives a good show of blue in May and there have also been found patches of white and pink sports. At around this time we get another show of blue, the Meadow Cranesbill – *Geranium pratense*. This plant was very scarce around the Estate and surrounding land in the 1980s but since the Council has stopped the chemical spraying of verges it has re-appeared and is developing some good stands on the roadsides and the edges of the woods. We found a double form in 1987 which lasted three to four years and several times a white and pink sport.

Both the everlasting peas are recorded on the Estate along ride edges, the native Narrow-leaved – *Lathyrus sylvestris* and the introduced broader leaved – *L. latifolius*. The broader leaved is only recorded in section 2 but the narrow leaved is found scattered in many sections and is occurring in profusion in Horn Wood since it was clear felled a few years back and now re-planted with hardwoods. It likes embankments and wood edges and the broad leaved sometimes produces a white sport.

Woody Nightshade (Bittersweet) – *Solanum dulcamara*. An attractive, native, climbing perennial. Common in hedges and along the edge of woodland rides, also on waste ground. The deep purple flowers can be seen from June to September and this long flowering period allows both flowers and ripe berries to be seen at the same time. The berries change from bright green through yellow to bright red and can produce a variety of colours along the twisting stem of the plant. Although parts of this plant are used medicinally the berries are poisonous and if ingested in sufficient quantity can prove fatal. The berries in ancient times were often mentioned in folklore tales. Necklaces made from the berries are reported as being found in Egyptian burial artefacts.

Yellow Flag – *Iris pseudoacorus* has been present for a long time around the edges of the larger Estate lakes and along Whiston Spinney but had not been seen on any of the bunker and woodland ponds. In 1992 a flower was spotted amongst other vegetation on a bunker pond. These pond edges have been gradually cleared since 1985 and the programme is almost complete so perhaps it was introduced by mud from the equipment used. It is slowly spreading so should continue to add some fresh colour to the ponds over the years.

We do not have a lot of old meadow amongst our woodlands but the MoD section does have a large (south) and a small area (west) which does give some good flora. The western meadow is especially good and shows typical meadow flora in great quantity. This meadow is managed sympathetically by the tenant farmer, in conjunction with English Nature, in order to give the best showing of flowers and allowing them to seed. In 1997 an English Nature representative found some Lousewort – *Pedicularis sylvatica* growing on bare soil along the top of a ditch on the wood edge. This plant had not been recorded in the county since 1950.-The following year the Botanical Society of the British Isles had a field meeting on the site in memory of the birthday of D C Druce (1850) the eminent county botanist who wrote the first county flora. Apart from seeing the lousewort again, other species were discovered and confirmed. Heath Spotted Orchid – *Dactylorchis maculata* and Heath Dog Violet – *Viola canina* both only a second recording for the county, also a variety of the Stemless/Dwarf Thistle – *Cirsium acaulon v caulescens* which differs in having a stem with branching buds.

The whole meadow was alive with colour; Betony both pink and white, devilsbit scabious, burnet saxifrage, greater burnet, goatsbeard, birds-foot trefoil and many others. Down a track leading off the meadow we found some Changing Forget-me-not – *Myosotis discolor ssp dubium*. It is safe to say that the day was enjoyed by all 21 members and I am sure that our own haversack rations were helped down by home made cake and tea supplied by the Range Warden's wife. The day was finished off by a quick dash cross the other meadow and into the woods to see the last remaining herb paris on flower.

The south meadow has Saw-wort – *Serratula tinctoria* growing, a rare county plant but is well established in parts of the Chase, a tall plant flowering July to September.

The Woolly Thistle – *Cirsium eriophorum* is an occasional plant in the county and we do have it at two locations on the Estate. It is a large flowered biennial normally growing to a height of 1.25 metres although we have photographed one specimen at a height of 2.5 metres. As always with thistles, the large flower head is a favourite with nectar seeking insects and wasps can often be seen grazing the woolly coating on the head of the plant. These tall thistles give a good supply of large seeds and are a great favourite with the finch family in the winter.

Ploughmans Spikenard – *Inula conyza* was found for the first time on the Estate in 1997 growing on the west bank of Engine Pond. This is an occasional plant of fairly open situations scattered mainly over the north of the county. The roots give off a noticeable fragrance when disturbed.

Nettle-leaved Bellflower – *Campanula trachelium* is another occasional native perennial of woodland growing to a height of 80cm. Clumps of this flower can be found scattered throughout the woods mainly on the ride edges and again white sports have been found.

The wet areas surrounding some of the ponds gives us the yellow of the Lesser Spearwort – *Ranunculus flammula* an occasional plant scattered through the county and the purple of the Purple-loosestrife – *Lythrum salicaria* a native, fairly abundant, waterside plant well established in the county. Water Plantain – *Alisma plantago-aquatica* is found on the muddy margins of the ponds and grows to about 1 metre high. The spindly flowering heads can be spotted easily amongst the other waterside vegetation and can give some very nice reflections on the still water of the pond. In winter the seed heads present a very nice picture when covered with a good hoar frost. The rare Narrow-leaved Water Plantain – *A. lanceolatum* grows on a pond in the north-east corner of the Estate. The leaves of this plant are very lanceolate and narrow at the base, it was first recorded by G Crawford a local botanist.

Reed Mace – *Typha latifolia*, often commonly and incorrectly called the bullrush, is plentiful wherever there is wet ground, ponds and ditches and can spread rapidly often taking over small shallow ponds and turning them into swamp. The familiar large brown seed heads are sometimes used in dried flower arrangements indoors but beware, if used, you could come down one morning to a nice fluffy covering over your carpet and curtains. The one not so often found is the Lesser Reed Mace – *T. angustifolia* which has a much slimmer head with the two parts of the flower head (male and female) separated by a section of the stem and this grows only on four of the bunker ponds. It is only an occasional plant in the county but can produce large stands where it does occur.

Soapwort – *Saponaria officinalis* a native perennial, fairly common on roadsides and hedgerows, mostly pink flowers but sometimes white and often a double form, up to 80 cm in height. The leaves and roots when boiled in water produce a lather which was used to wash wool and the plant can often be found growing in large quantities in the vicinity of wool mills. The lather can also be added to bath water as a remedy for eczema and other skin conditions.

Fleabane – *Pulicaria dysenterica* and Sneezewort – *Achillea ptarmica* are both plants of damp habitats and along ditches in woodland and meadows. They are occasional plants and seem to be decreasing due to drainage and grassland improvements, sneezewort being the more scarce of the two. The ponds and wet areas in our woodland are very favoured by these two plants.

Gromwell – *Lithospermum officinale* a native perennial of hedges and wood edges usually occurring in small numbers and not common in the county. Small white flowers in June and July which produce small white very hard nutlets that show up the dead plant in the late autumn and winter. These nutlets when pulverised were used in olden times, mixed with a glass of wine, to cure bladder stones.

APPEARANCE OF WILD FLOWERS

	JAN	FEB	MAR	APR	MAY	JUN	JUL	AUG	SEP	OCT	NOV	DEC
Lesser Celandine (Ranunculus ficaria)			■	■	■							
Primrose (Primula vulgaris)			■	■	■							
Coltsfoot (Tussilago farfara)			■	■								
Wood Anemone (Anemone nemorosa)	■	■	■	■	■							
Dandelion (Taraxacum officinale)			■	■	■							
Dog Violet (Viola riviniana)				■	■							
Cowslip (Primula veris)				■	■							
Lords & Ladies (Arum maculatum)			■	■								
Bluebell (Endymion non-scriptus)			■	■	■							
Cow Parsley (Anthriscus sylvestris)				■	■	■						
Early Purple Orchid (Orchis mascula)				■	■	■						
Red Campion (Silene dioica)					■	■	■	■				
Ragged Robin (Lychnis flos-cuculi)					■	■	■					
Bugle (Ajuga repans)					■	■	■					
Scarlet Pimpernel (Anagallis arvensis)						■	■	■				
Meadow Buttercup (Ranunculus acris)				■	■	■	■	■	■	■		
Dog Rose (Rosa canina)						■	■	■				
Ox-eye Daisy (Leucanthemum vulgare)					■	■	■	■				
Field Poppy (Papaver rhoeas)					■	■	■	■				
Foxglove (Digitalis purpurea)						■	■	■				
Com. Spotted Orchid (Dactylorhiza fuchsii)						■	■	■				
Yellow Water-lily (Nuphar lutea)					■	■	■	■				
Fleabane (Pulicaria dysenterica)							■	■	■			
Rosebay Willowherb (Chamaerion angustifolium)						■	■	■	■			
Hemp Agrimony (Eupatorium cannabinum)						■	■	■	■			
Nettle-leaved Bellflower (Campanula trachelium)							■	■	■			
Woolly Thistle (Cirsium eriophorum)							■	■	■			

Musk Mallow – *Malva moschata*. This plant was not seen at all for the first few years but appeared along the edges of a rail track in Sane Copse when it was cleared and opened up in 1990. As this programme continued so these flowers started to appear and they are still with us today. However, due to the re-growth of brambles and coarse grasses on the sides of these tracks, they are not so plentiful now but will no doubt increase whenever clearing is done.

Hemp Agrimony – *Eupatorium cannabinum* is a native perennial of marshes and damp places, occasional but can be common where it does occur. This tall flower with its pink composite head, blooming in late July, is very attractive to bees and butterflies. Indeed, it was on the flower of this plant that we saw our first white-letter hairstreak butterfly.

Orange Hawkweed – *Hieracium aurantiacum* sometimes called Fox and Cubs. This is an introduced perennial and garden escape and is becoming established on roadsides and hedgerows. We have two locations for this plant, a farm entrance and a small patch in the middle of Sane Copse.

Orange Mullein – *Verbascum phlomoides* is a natural biennial occasionally found on waste and bare ground and dry stony ground. This was recorded in the disused sand pit in 1998. The flowers are a bright orange-yellow in woolly racemes, flowering July to September. The Common or Great Mullein – *V. thapsus* is an occasional plant which pops up here and there on old railway tracks and the like. This has been recorded in three of our sections and is found throughout most of the county.

White Mignonette – *Reseda alba* an introduction often found on waste ground mainly in the south of England, It was recorded on the main LMS rail track in 1981 but hasn't been seen since a part of the track was scraped for aggregate.

I have only mentioned those flowers that are considered to be some of the highlights and more interesting of our vascular plants, a complete list of species is given at the back of this book. The pleasure and enjoyment it has given to the Wild Bunch cannot be described here, nor the hard work carried out by the botanists amongst us.

To those of you keen to record plants and who have a patch of your own somewhere, or have access to, then keep going, get off the beaten track and down on your hands and knees. Visit all areas at all times and never go out without a notebook, a hand lens and perhaps a small packet of band-aid.

Non-flowering plants

Three important groups of non-flowering plants must be mentioned before moving on to the fauna. These are the ferns, fungi and bryophytes. These three groups tend to be under recorded because they do not flower and are often more difficult to identify. True they don't flower in the generally accepted term but they do all produce spores and the changing shapes and colours that occur during this process is well worth observing.

Two of our ferns worth mentioning here are the Adders Tongue – *Ophioglossum vulgatum* and the Harts Tongue – *Phyllitis scolopendrium*. Adders Tongue could perhaps be mistaken for a flower in bud because of its shape but the stem only produces spores. It is found on damp meadow land in May to August but because of its size and leaf shape it is not an easy one to spot amongst the grass although it can reach a height of 20cm. It is a rapidly declining plant due to the continuing loss of its habitat. However I am pleased to say that it is actually increasing on our MoD meadows.

Harts Tongue, a native fern growing in woods and on shady walls or rocks. In the early 1980s there was a nice old stone wall just outside the Estate boundary by the main line rail track which had a good coverage of this fern but the wall was sold for stone and the ferns have not re-appeared.

Our next sighting was in the MoD area growing inside a manhole (the MoD sites have dozens of manholes, all uncovered) and a few years later we found another manhole with the fern growing in it. In 1994 another two plants were found growing in a manhole in Sane Copse (ex MoD). We were a bit concerned when, for safety reasons the Army decided to cover all their manholes. However, all turned out well as after consultation between the MoD Land Agents and English Nature it was agreed that the two containing the ferns would be covered with an open grille which would allow them to continue growing. The next sighting was in 1996 when we started to survey the old ironstone quarry near Whiston where it was found growing on the exposed rock face. The spores on the back of these leaves are the food source for a micro moth – *Psychoides verhuella* which makes a small case of the spores as camouflage when it wanders about feeding on the spore ridges. This moth is generally found in the western region of the country but it has been recorded once in Bedfordshire so if anybody wants a challenge, go to it!

When recording first started in the woods Bracken – *Pteridium aquilinum* was only found in three places, MoD, Denton Wood and Ravenstone Road Copse and only in small patches. Over the last twenty years these patches have increased in size. The MoD patch has trebled in area and now covers approximately 0.2 hectares. This fern is now spreading into other parts of our woodland and could become a further serious threat to our woodland ground-floor flowers. It can be poisonous to live stock if eaten in quantity but is normally avoided by cattle, sheep or rabbits which enables it to spread by its far-reaching rhizomes into good grazing land thus reducing its value.

Fungi are a very large group to study (Mycology) and not the easiest of species to identify. There are numerous books relating to fungi, some good, some not very useful. Some fungi can be readily identified by the use of colour plates but most need other means as well, i.e smell, spore colour and shape and for this you do need a microscope and the ability to carry out simple chemical tests. The problem with relying just on colour plates, assuming that they are accurately produced, depends on the state of the growth at the time the specimen was photographed as they can change greatly during their growing time. Wet days and dry days also greatly affect their colouring. But please don't be put off; try to find someone who has knowledge of this group and be prepared to file a number of them under LBJ (little brown job). I always hesitate to recommend books but amongst the many available would suggest for starters – Mushrooms and Other Fungi of Great Britain by Roger Phillips and published by Pan Books, also Encyclopaedia of Fungi of Britain and Europe by Michael Jordan, published by David and Charles.

We all felt that fungi were interesting and fascinating in their life habits and they also make good photographic subjects. It was for that reason that initially fungi were down to me. After all, it's no good having a nice picture if you don't know what it is. I managed reasonably well by using the LBJ file a lot but was very pleased when we were joined by Jerry Cooper. He is a member of the British Mycological Society whose forte is micro fungi and while he was with us recorded two new national records and nine new county records, The new national records were both mildews – *Sawadaea tulaasnei* on acer in 1991 and in 1992 – *Circinotrichum macculliforme* on plane (previously recorded in the USA). Unfortunately Jerry has now left us and moved on to pastures new and, needless to say, new fungi records are few and far between these days.

The bit that we see above ground is the fruiting body. The fungus itself is a mass of hyphae attached to mycelium buried out of sight in the food substrate mainly wood and soil. Some of these fruiting bodies of the mushrooms and toadstools are over in a few days while some can last a week or more, brackets will hang on for months or even years. The purpose served by fungi is to break down dead or dying material, mostly vegetable but some animal. These are the saprophytes, the few that feed on living material are termed parasitic.

There are three main groups of fungi which most people will see on their walks through the woods and fields. Basidiomycetes (spore droppers) those with stalks and caps; polypores, brackets, puffballs and jelly fungi; ascomycetes, (spore shooters), morels, cup fungi and truffles.

Although some fungi are edible and indeed a number of these are now being sold in supermarkets, never eat any from the field unless identification has been confirmed by an expert and they must always be cooked.

One horror story (almost) that I experienced was in 1992. A group of Wood mushrooms – *Agaricus silvicola* were found in Olney Lane End and these are good to eat. One member of our group decided he would enhance his bacon in the morning and picked some (he is still with us!). Whilst this was going on I wandered away, still looking, and found about a metre away a dozen or so Death Caps – *Amanita phalloides* this being the first record of this species for the Estate. Looking down on the caps of these two species they are not dissimilar, however the Death Cap does have white gills underneath. I went back the next day to photograph the Death Cap (I had used up my film the previous day). There was a man and a woman walking up the ride towards me carrying a trug containing some fungi. After pointing out that they should not be in the woods, I enquired as to their reason for gathering fungi – study or culinary – and might I see their gatherings (in case they had found some that I hadn't). He said that they were for eating and that he had just found some wood mushrooms. This was true, he had cleared the remainder of the patch that we had found the previous day. He had also picked the Death Caps! I had quite a job to convince him – they were growing together, you could peel them, they would be alright when they were cooked he remarked. Luckily by then I had managed to frighten his wife sufficiently and she threw them all in the ditch and with the usual wifely comments that her husband was always doing daft things, dragged him back down the ride.

Oh what a foolish man! I shudder to think of the local newspaper headlines that could have been. An extreme case maybe but my advice is enjoy the beauty of fungi and leave them to multiply. I do not propose to recommend edibility in the following pages, unless I have eaten them myself.

Autumn is usually the start of the fungi season although some species can be found throughout the year. The quantities found each season vary greatly according to climatic conditions. They seem to do best in wet humid weather. There are some that won't spore until they have been touched by frost.

Probably the most prolific fungus in our woods is the Honey Fungus – *Armillaria mellea* also known as the boot-lace fungus. It is a very variable ochre to dark brown colour with a cap up to 15cm across. It grows in dense clusters around the trunks of mainly deciduous trees and sometimes conifers. It spreads by long black cords (rhizomorphs) which look like long black boot-laces which can be found beneath the bark of infected trees. This fungus is considered one of the most dangerous parasites to trees causing severe white rot and eventual death, This fungus is responsible for the killing of large quantities of trees and there is no known cure.

Another widespread fungus which leaves its signs over many oak wood floors is the Green Woodcup – *Chlorosplenium aeruginascens*. This is the one that leaves the blue-green stained wood scattered on the floor but is seldom seen in its small green cup form up to 10mm across in late September. It is found mainly on fallen branches of oak. The mycelium growing through the wood stains it blue-green and is known as 'green oak' and was used in the manufacture of Tunbridge ware, a form of decorative marquetry.

The Aniseed Toadstool – *Clitocybe fragrans* is a pale blue-green colour and can often be detected by its sweet smell, it can be found solitary or in troops on the soil of broad-leaved woods. The Amethyst Deceiver – *Laccaria amethystea* is an attractive small toadstool up to 10cm high with a cap up to 5cm and of a deep purplish colour, it can be found in varying numbers in both conifer and deciduous woods. Velvet Shank – *Flammulina velutipes* shows a tan-yellow cap, dark in the centre and with the stem densely velvety and dark. It grows in large clusters on dead deciduous trees and is quite striking on a bare January day. A similar fungus which grows in large clusters on dead stumps is the Sulphur Tuft – *Hypholoma fasciculare*, a sulphur yellow cap and stem with flesh of the same colour when broken, very noticeable and can be found all the year round.

Wax Caps – *Hygrocybes sp.* are usually quite striking colours of red, orange, yellow and green and the cap is often pointed and slimy to the touch. They are found in meadows and rides and are not that common around the Estate but are worth looking for amongst the grass in late summer to autumn.

Milk Caps – *Lactarius sp.* are a group of some 56 species ranging through colours of white, cream, tawny to olive-black but they will all exude a whitish milk when broken which tastes very hot and peppery. They are mostly associated with woods and are sometimes found growing on other fungi.

The *Russula* family is a very large one, some 112 species. They are fleshy, often robust mushrooms and most have brightly coloured caps, often fading very quickly, of predominantly red and purple but there are also yellow and green-grey caps. Although robust the flesh is very brittle and breaks very easily and more often than not the caps are off or broken when you find them.

The *Agaricus* family contain the mushrooms that can be bought in the shops. Most of this family are edible but beware those that bruise yellow. There are about 40 species in Britain, some in woods but mostly in grass habitats. The one being found most often is the Horse Mushroom – *Agaricus arvensis* which can grow to a large size of up to 20cm across the cap and are usually easily spotted amongst the grass, especially if the field has been grazed. There used to be many more about than there are today and it is rare these days to find a field covered with these mushrooms. The liming of grass fields was probably the cause of this decline. The largest one I have found was 28cm (11”). I fried it whole and it went just over the edge of the plate, an egg in the middle (sunnyside up) and a slice of bacon completed the picture.

Plums and Custard – *Tricholomopsis rutilans*, this name being a good description of its colour, is readily found in conifer woodland growing on old stumps or very old piles of stacked pine logs. The cap is up to 12cm across with a stem up to 6cm and it can be found from late summer to late autumn.

The Oyster Mushroom – *Pleurotus ostreatus* is quite a common mushroom often found in large clusters on fallen or standing trunks of deciduous trees at any time of the year. It tends to form tiers of blue-grey caps up to 14cm across. It can appear as if it were a bracket type as the stem is short and often not clearly visible when growing out from a trunk. This is one species that has now become popular and is frequently sold in supermarkets.

Before finishing with the *Agaricus* (toadstool) type, another very noticeable and very prolific group in our woodland is the *Clitocybe* family, the large ones *C.geotropa* and *C. giganteus* are seen very easily from a distance with their large white concave caps. They are described as growing in troops or rings and I think that the word troop fits them perfectly when you see a line of them extending along the woodland floor, sometimes as long as 5 metres. *C. giganteus* is the largest with a cap reaching 30cm across but is only occasionally recorded on the Estate, *C. geotropa* has a cap up to 20cm and is plentiful in all the Estate woodlands.

Other noticeable groups that like to grow in rings are the parasol mushrooms, *Macrolepiota procera* and the smaller shaggy *M. rhacodes* being the less common of the two. The largest circle of *M. procera* we have found was in 1990 and had a diameter of 10 metres.

The *Boletaceae* are a family of about 36 species and are mainly associated with trees. Although they have a cap and stem they do not have gills underneath but a series of tubes (pores) on the underside of the cap looking rather like a sponge. The top of the cap is usually dry but may go viscid in wet weather. They occur in many colours and most have thick bulbous stems which have no ring. They are not very prolific in our woods and we have very few records from this family.

The next group to be readily seen are the brackets and the most noticeable of these must be the Birch Polypore or Razor-strop – *Piptoporus betulinus* which only grows on birch. Wherever you see dead birches about then you can guarantee to see them, large brackets 10-20cm across, mostly of uniform shape, growing up the tree. Although seen all the year round it only sporates in the late summer and like all brackets it does not have gills but tubes.

Old brackets can become very woody and sometimes last several years on the tree. Some are quite small and some very large and strong enough to hold the weight of a person. I have a photograph of George standing on a specimen of *Rigidoporus ulmarius* growing at the base of an old horse chestnut tree.

One very common and colourful bracket is the Many-zoned Polypore – *Coriolus versicolor*. The top is very noticeably concentrically zoned in varying colours with white/cream margins, usually growing on stumps in overlapping tiered groups. With age the tops of these brackets can have additional colours from algae which sometimes completely covers them with hues of green. This particular bracket dries very well and can be used in dried flower arrangements. The best way to dry fungi is to purchase one of the small clothes airers designed to clip on to a house radiator and place a small meshed wire tray on it. They should dry in a few days (with the radiator on) but toadstool types will mostly distort when dried.

The Maze Gill – *Daedalea quercina* is quite distinctive as the maze-like tubes below sometimes grow downwards giving the appearance of organ pipes. The corky cap is up to 20cm across and occasionally grows in shelved groups although it is mainly found singly. It is virtually restricted to dead oak and is fairly common.

Other fungi of interesting shapes and sizes are the puff-balls, commonly found and all similar in appearance. The largest is the Giant Puff-ball – *Calvatia gigantea* which we have only recorded twice on the Estate both in the Ravenstone Road Copse area. These puff-balls can reach a size of 80cm across although the largest we have found was only 33cm. Unlike the other smaller puff-balls, these, when ripe, separate from their mycelial cord (root) leaving it free to be blown about by the wind scattering its spores as it goes. The others, of which there are many, remain attached to the ground when ripe but the outer skin ruptures at the top and waits for something to knock it, rain or a foraging pheasant, causing the spores to puff out at the top. This can also be caused by very strong winds.

Stinkhorns, of which there are two, start off life as an 'egg' buried just below the surface of the ground which will erupt and push out the fruit body which can take as little as two hours to reach full size. The Common Stinkhorn – *Phallus impudicus* is the biggest and can grow to a height of 24cm and it can often be smelt before you can see it. We have sometimes spent several minutes trying to trace the source of the smell, very foetid, without success as they can often be growing in the middle of a bramble thicket. This smell of rotten meat attracts flies and bluebottles which feed off the mucous covered head thus distributing the spore, the empty head shows a lattice pattern. The other small Dog Stinkhorn – *Mutinus caninus* has a more slender stem, often curved, which shows orange at the tip when all the spores have gone. The smell from these is only very slight. It is not a common fungus, the first small group was found in 1981 and there were no further records until 1998 and 1999 when it occurred in profusion in a conifer block.

Coming down to some of the smaller species, the most colourful and diverse shapes are probably the horn/club types and the coral-like ones which are usually found growing on wood or bare soil.

Other interesting shapes are the morels which are stalked with a small lattice/honeycomb cap. The one most recorded on the Estate is *Morchella semilibera* which crops up in grassy areas but not always in the same place. In 1996 a new county record was discovered on our first visit to the Firs quarry, *Verpa conica*, which likes a hawthorn habitat but it had gone from the site by 1998. Then there are the cup-shaped species ranging in size from 2-10cm usually growing on the ground or straw with generally neutral colours. The orange peel and small disc types are usually bright orange or red and very noticeable.

Probably one of the most interesting but seldom seen fungus is Ergot – *Claviceps purpurea* which is a disease of cereals and shows as a small blackish cucumber protruding from an ear of corn or rye, up to 2cm long and about 5mm thick. This has occasionally been found in our surrounding cereal fields. This used to be a serious pest in the olden days when the crop was cut by scythes and milled by a local miller. Mixed in with the flour in large enough quantities it could induce ergotism which causes some very nasty symptoms often ending in death. Whilst these incidents have been rare in Britain, they were quite common on the continent, especially in France.

Fungus forays are often organised with local and distant natural history societies travelling to the Chase to search for and identify the fungi found on the day. These parties, sometimes a coachload, are usually led by an 'expert' and the object is for the rest of the party to learn about fungi. These days, thanks to TV programmes, the emphasis seems unfortunately to be changing to culinary interests. These forays are always good fun if only from the variety of containers used to collect them in (a wicker basket or a trug is best) and of course there is always someone who picks the very specimen that you have been searching for for a long time so that you could photograph it!

The lunch break is always an interesting period where, apart from eating their sandwiches, they gather round the various collections to try and identify their catch. Most of them can be dealt with on site with the help of reference books and the expert and more knowledgeable members of the group although a few specimens do have to be taken home to determine the exact species. Your field bag should always contain a packet of wet wipes just in case you have handled any poisonous fungi, use before eating sandwiches! Some people wear the disposable gloves available from chemists when picking their specimens. The end result of these and other field meetings is that the Estate gets a complete list of the species found to add to their existing records.

One of the conditions regarding any field meeting held on Estate land is that the leader of the group has agreed and is responsible for making sure that all records of the species found are sent in to the Estate office.

One last green chapter before we move on to the Estate fauna is a group that are seen everywhere but are often disregarded due to the difficulty for the layman to identify them. They have their own beauty and as a mass often enhance a woodland or stonework scene and these are the mosses and liverworts. The order Bryophytes cover both of these groups which form an important part of our ecosystem but are often overlooked when management or conservation programmes are formed. The Estate as a whole has very varied habitats some of which are eminently suited for bryophytes and these have produced a very rich flora. Currently 138 mosses and 18 liverworts have been recorded. As already mentioned, the Chase is usually very wet and, coupled with our many ponds, provides very good bryophyte habitats, the best specimens being found in damp situations. Apart from a good woodland mix with rides other terrains can also be suited; old buildings and walls of stone or brick, concrete building structures, gravel and cinder tracks, sand pits and arable land. Areas that are particularly rich in mosses and liverworts are those which are relatively undisturbed, damp and sheltered. Some of our best areas are the Firs Quarry, the old pumphouse by the sand pit, Dinglederry – an area just inside the south-east boundary of the Chase and extending into

Bucks and Whiston Spinney, the latter being a very notable site in the county. Each of these sites contains old elder trees which are particularly good hosts and provide sites for such as *Cryphaea heteromalla* and *Orthotrichum tenellum*.

The Cambridge group of the British Bryological Society (BBS) has made two visits to the Estate. In 1989 there was an excursion to Denton Wood and the MoD section. The latter site contained the nationally scarce aquatic liverwort *Ricciocarpus natans* and was recorded by the late Dr H L K Whitehouse; it was a new county record. At the suggestion of Dr Whitehouse a search was made on all the other ponds in the area and it was found on most of them. In 1998 the Society also visited the sand pit and Whiston Spinney where several noteworthy species were found. The Firs Quarry and Whiston Spinney was first visited by the Wild Bunch in 1996 and it was immediately recognised as being a very valuable bryophyte site due to the large numbers of old elders covering the banks of the stream running through it coupled with the broken canopy letting in light. 24 species were recorded on that first walk.

One exciting find that day, although we did not know it at the time, was on an old mud mortar wall. This type of wall is rapidly disappearing these days as the mud is being replaced by cement.

We had retired to an old barn (Nats Barn) on the hill to get out of the very cold wind and eat our haversack rations in some shelter. Never one to miss an opportunity, Frances searched the old stone wall for any mosses and some small patches were found. A small piece was taken home for identification. This turned out to be a nationally scarce species and not recorded in the county for over 50 years. This specimen was sent to the National Recorder who confirmed that it was indeed *Pterygoneurum ovatum*. Once confirmed we visited the barn again to photograph the moss and identify the site. The Estate and tenant farmer were notified of this find so that the site will remain undisturbed and hopefully the moss patch will prosper.

As mentioned, 1998 saw a visit by the BBS to this area and its finds certainly extended our species list. The star of the area (*P. ovatum*) was again photographed and became the subject of a presentation made to the Department of Plant Sciences, University of Cambridge by the late Dr H L K Whitehouse at the annual conversatzione of the Cambs. Natural History Society in June of that year. A quote from his accompanying notes is given below:

"*Pterygoneurum ovatum* used to be frequent in Cambridgeshire but now seems to be extinct in the county. Its decline is usually attributed to the loss of earth capped walls, which were a favourite habitat, but this does not account for its disappearance from other habitats such as chalk banks. Its decline coincided with the disappearance of the horse from the English roads and this may be significant."

The MoD site has produced the liverwort *Lepidozia reptans* and Cold Oak Copse the moss *Ulota phyllantha* both of which are very scarce in the county. Also two new county records were achieved for the mosses *Bryum dunense* and *Herzogiella seligeri*.

Plant vouchers for new county records are deposited in the BBS herbarium at the National Museum for Wales, Cardiff.

Whilst not included in the above order, there is one other group which is plentiful – the algae. Again, being mainly microscopic organisms they are overlooked but one that we have recorded is *Nostoc commune* and that because it is a large noticeable species. It looks like a limp/boiled lettuce leaf, blue/green in colour and about the size of a saucer. We had seen it in patches for some time on the disused railtrack where the cinder had become scraped away exposing the bare clay. One day we had the opportunity to have it identified by Professor Alan Brook of Buckingham University who stated that it was rarely recorded nationally.

Also included in this group are the stoneworts (*Chara*) which are found in most of our bunker ponds and which have produced three species, identified as a result of a survey carried out by Dr P M Wade of Loughborough University in 1996.

The study of these lesser known plants needs considerable patience, while some do grow on trees most are on ditch banks and the like, often under thick shrub and bramble cover and difficult to get at. You will always need a good hand lens, small envelopes to place collected specimens in and a small palette knife to remove specimens from difficult subtrates. It is also useful to have someone with you to help you out of some of the deeper slippery ditches!

MoD Bunkers

The bunkers are probably the most unique features of the Chase and have certainly given us habitats and species that we would not normally have had. The bunker building itself is just a rectangular brick box with a reinforced concrete roof, supported inside by pillars. As additional protection for site personnel an earth embankment was built around most bunkers. Only those containing non-explosive material were left without these earthworks. These 'blast walls' are all approximately the same size to a height of 2.5-3.5m and were constructed by excavating the surrounding clay leaving behind borrow pits. These soon filled with water and became ponds. Over the entire MoD areas there are 44 bunkers, 9 of which do not have these surrounding earthworks and therefore no ponds. The ponds that surround each bunker vary in number from two to six although there are two bunkers where the pond is continuous all the way round. The total number of separate ponds over both sites is 82 plus 37 totalling 119.

The pH values have been recorded on all individual ponds, the measurement being taken using a Whatman pH Sensor and the readings ranged from 7.05-8.0 with an average of 7.7. A chemical analysis of the water was carried out on a sample of six ponds across both areas which shows us a good neutral rain water content with no run off from the surrounding agricultural land.

Initially we had mapped out each bunker, with its compass position, schematically at a scale of 2cm = 10 metres so that we knew the number of and the general shape and position of each pond. This was done for both areas (over a period of time!). We later decided it would be useful if we had more knowledge of these ponds, for possible future and more detailed studies, so in 1992 we purchased a small two seater dinghy. This has enabled us to accurately map out all the individual ponds in relation to the bunker and plumb their depths, starting with Sane Copse (37 ponds). All the ponds are very steep sided, except sometimes at the ends, which makes them dangerous should you try to wade in. The pond bottoms are relatively level and firm and are covered with about 30cm of silt from the fallen leaves and twigs. The depths range from one to four metres the average being about two metres.

The aquatic plants are much the same in all the ponds, predominantly Broad-leaved Pondweed – *Potamogeton natans*, three species of Stoneworts – *Chara sp.* with the marginal vegetation being mainly Reed Mace – *Typha latifolia*, Bulrush – *Scirpus lacustris* and Reed – *Phragmites australis*. Three-spined Sticklebacks – *Gastrosteus aculeatus* are the only fish to be found naturally in the ponds except for one when in 1990 some Roach – *Rutilus rutilus* were introduced, without authorisation, into one pond in Sane Copse. We have also recorded the less common form of the stickleback, the scaleless *G. leirus*.

Some of the ponds on the MoD site still being used by the Army do have introduced fish. The first bunker (B8) nearest to the barrack block had goldfish, roach and gudgeon introduced during the war years and also the White Water-lily – *Nymphaea alba* was planted. One can only assume the Commanding Officer of that time liked a bit of fishing. Since then three other ponds have had goldfish released into them. These fish came from the very large static water tank in Simpson Barracks when it was drained for repair work. The heron soon picked off the coloured goldfish but

<u>YARDLEY CHASE – Section 3 (MoD)</u>

Average pH reading for each bunker area:-

Bunker	pH	Bunker	pH	Bunker	pH
A1	7.4	B1	7.73	C2	7.72
A2	7.5	B2	7.57	C4	7.52
A3	7.67	B3	8.0	C5	7.77
A6	7.9	B4	7.55	C6	7.62
A7	8.0	B5	7.46	C7	7.43
A8	7.62	B6	7.7	C8	7.46
A10	7.57	B7	7.05	SE Em. pond 7.7	
A11	7.5	B8	7.43	Quarry pond 7.35	
A12	7.7	B9	7.52		

Average overall site pH is 7.6 ranging from 6.6 (B7) to 8.2 (B1) on individual ponds

Chemical analysis of water from selected ponds in 1988 using Park pond as standard.

	Std. C/A 1	3 A12-S	3 B3-E	3 C5-N
Conductivity	500 mimos	400 mimos	300 mimos	430 mimos
pH	7.89	7.49	7.9	7.82
Cadmium	nil	nil	nil	nil
Lead	nil	nil	nil	nil
Copper	nil	nil	nil	nil
Chrome	nil	nil	nil	nil
Calcium	80 mg/lit	72 mg/lit	49 mg/lit	67 mg/lit
Nitrates	50 mg/lit	10 mg/lit	10 mg/lit	10 mg/lit
Sulphates	400 mg/lit	300 mg/lit	300 mg/lit	300 mg/lit

82 ponds.

<u>YARDLEY CHASE</u> – Section 4

Average pH reading for each bunker area:-

Bunker	pH	Bunker	pH
D1	7.7	E2	7.65
D2	7.6	E3	7.66
D3	7.75	E4	7.55
D5	7.85	E7	7.87
D6	7.8	E8	7.7
D7	7.85		

Average overall site pH is 7.72 ranging from 7.4 (E8) to 8.0 (D6) on individual ponds

Chemical analysis of water from selected ponds in 1988 using Park pond as standard.

	Std. C/A 1	3 D2-E	3 D6-N	3 E4-S
Conductivity	500 mimos	260 mimos	340 mimos	265 mimos
pH	7.89	7.46	7.85	7.59
Cadmium	nil	nil	nil	nil
Lead	nil	nil	nil	nil
Copper	nil	nil	nil	nil
Chrome	nil	nil	nil	nil
Calcium	80 mg/lit	38 mg/lit	61 mg/lit	50 mg/lit
Nitrates	50 mg/lit	10 mg/lit	10 mg/lit	10 mg/lit
Sulphates	400 mg/lit	300 mg/lit	300 mg/lit	300 mg/lit

37 ponds.

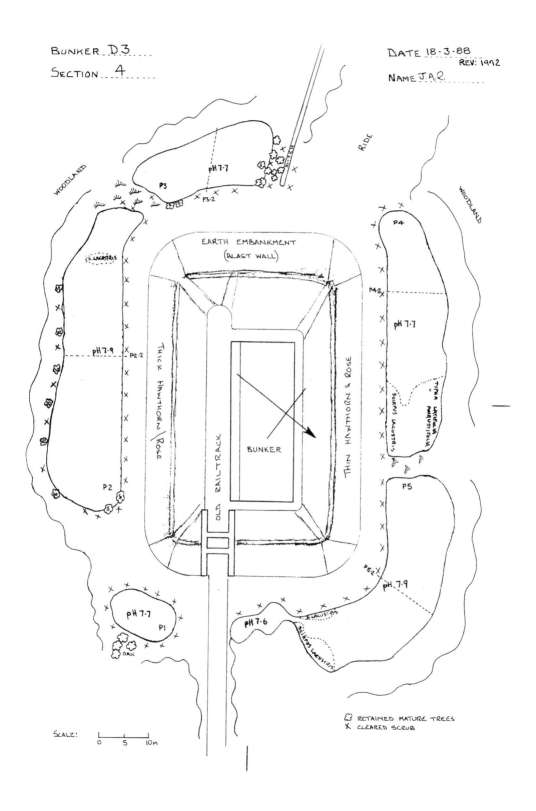

BUNKER D3 ....
SECTION ... 4 ......

DATE 18·3·88
REV: 1992
NAME J.A.R. ....

WOODLAND

pH 7·7
P3
P3·2
DITCH

RIDE

WOODLAND

P4
P4·2
pH 7·7

S. LACUSTRIS

pH 7·9   P2·2

THICK HAWTHORN / ROSE

EARTH EMBANKMENT
(BLAST WALL)

BUNKER

OLD RAILTRACK

THIN HAWTHORN & ROSE

TYPHA LATIFOLIA ANGUSTIFOLIA

SCIRPUS LACUSTRIS

P2
S
S

P5
P5·2
pH 7·9

pH 7·7
P1

pH 7·6
S. LACUSTRIS
SCIRPUS LACUSTRIS

OAK

☘ RETAINED MATURE TREES
✕ CLEARED SCRUB

SCALE:
0   5   10m

Pond Water Depths

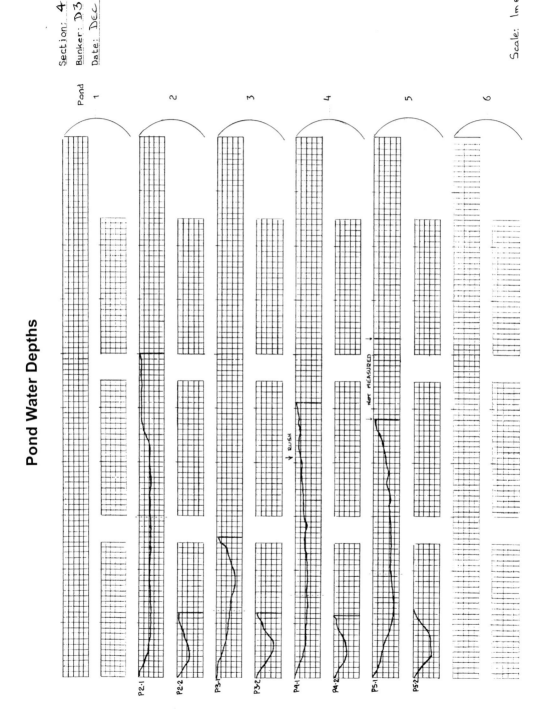

there still remains some carp and reverted goldfish. All these fish additions have, of course, affected the other aquatic life present in these ponds prior to their introduction e.g dragonflies and newts. The full mapping exercise has not been carried out on the active MoD site due to the considerable training activity going on.

Entomology

Moving now into the insect world it is only fair to say that some orders have been well studied and recorded whilst others, due to lack of expertise, have been under recorded. Sometimes we have been lucky enough to obtain the welcome services of an expert for a day or two to help cover these lesser studied orders. Unfortunately their services are always in demand so we have to be content with the few days they are able to give us.

Lepidoptera is certainly the most studied order amongst us by day and by night. In daylight we are able to record the butterflies and day flying moths but the majority of moths are only about at night so we have to use a light lure. Starting with the butterflies of which we have recorded 34 species on the Estate, we have some scarce and uncommon species, I started off my story with a purple emperor and I have the photograph to prove it! This at the time got us all very excited as the surrounding woodland was the ideal text book habitat but we have not seen one since. It stayed on our records until 1993 but was then removed as we all felt certain that it had been a released specimen. People, for various reasons, do release specimens into the wild and this action can cause problems for the County Recorder and others. If any British species are released into the wild this fact should always be notified to the County Recorder and the local Wildlife Trust. Alien species of any form of wildlife should never be released, as they often become serious pests. Salcey Forest seems to be the favourite location for these releases as it has public access and for the stronger flying insects it is no distance from there to the Chase. In 1981 I photographed a Heath Fritillary butterfly – *Melitaea atalia* on the disused main line rail track This to me was an obvious release as this butterfly has not been recorded in the area and we did not include it in our records.

Probably the first butterfly to be seen each year is the Brimstone – *Gonepteryx rhamni*. A sunny day or two in January or February can tempt this insect out of its hibernation for a brief flight but April/May is when you start to see them in any number. The adults which emerge from the pupa in August need to feed up on nectar to build themselves up for their winter hibernation in solitary confinement, a favourite site being thick ivy. The first warm days of spring will cause them to re-emerge and seek out any source of nectar to replace their lost energies and then seek out a female to mate. She will then seek out the nearest buckthorn bushes. Alder buckthorn has not been recorded on the Estate so our breeding is done on the purging buckthorn and the larva can usually be found laying along the midrib of a leaf.

Our rarest butterfly is the Black Hairstreak – *Strymonidia pruni* which has two known sites on the Estate. This is a nationally rare insect and only occurs in a few locations in the east midlands forest belt ranging from Oxford to Peterborough. Only about 30 colonies remain today and these are all regularly monitored by various wildlife groups.

Old blackthorn hedges in a sunny position are its chosen habitat, usually facing south or west. The breeding areas are often quite small and their sedentary behaviour does not make them the easiest insect to spot, the flight period is only six weeks between June and July. The cutting of blackthorn hedges where the butterfly is known to reside has to be carefully planned and monitored. Most hedge cutting is carried out during winter/early spring. Where the blackthorn hedge is a known black hairstreak habitat it needs to be managed at a different time. Late May – June is the pupal period of this butterfly, the safest time to cut the hedge. All the cut brash should be left laying at the base of the hedge so that any emerging butterflies will have immediate access to their required habitat.

The adult butterfly usually keeps high up in the hedge as its favourite food is aphid honeydew but it does sometimes come down to feed on bramble or privet flowers. Because of its normally high position in the hedge it is not the easiest butterfly to photograph and I recall a day in 1993 when the FC informed Andy and me that Anglia TV wanted to do an article on the black hairstreak and were arriving that day. Andy chose the best site where he had seen them the previous day (not on the Estate) and it was not a very sunny day when they arrived. The cameraman was very lucky that day. Even with his large lenses the small subject needed to be no more that a couple of metres away but one very obliging butterfly decided to come down low and even probed for an egg laying site. He got his picture. Binoculars are necessary for the positive identification of these high flying adults.

Apart from the black we do have three other hairstreaks recorded on the Estate; white letter, purple and green.

The White Letter – *Strymonidia w-album* feeds on the flowers and leaves of the elm family *Ulmus* and is particularly fond of wych elm. The elm population has been considerably depleted over these past years but we had one wood, Old Pond Close, where wych elm had maintained a good population. It was here that the butterfly was first recorded as breeding but over the years they have moved out into the patches of elm in the main Chase woodland, possibly using an old connecting hedge as a corridor. This 500 metre long hedge connects Old Pond Close with the Chase. It is an old hedge having been left when the area in between was clear felled, probably in the early 1700s. The hedge contains elm which has grown up to a reasonable size and also other hedgerow species providing nectar-bearing flowers. There is a small pond halfway along and the hedge has not been severely clipped. The adult butterfly spends most of its time on the larger elm trees usually in sunny positions, on ride edges, feeding on aphid honeydew but it will also come down to hemp agrimony and thistle. July is their main flight period.

The Purple - *Quercusia quercus* is our commonest and is found in all of our woodland sections containing large oaks. Although often abundant they usually keep up in the canopy, especially if there is ash about. On a sunny day they can be found feeding on bramble and other flowers when the iridescent purple of the wings can be seen.

The Green – *Callophrys rubi* is our scarcest being infrequently recorded on the main line rail track area. Colonies are usually small in number and they prefer warm sheltered habitats; railway cuttings are good. Its food plant is birdsfoot trefoil and sometimes dogwood, both of these plants being readily found along the track. It has quite a long flight period, end of April to the beginning of July.

The Wood White – *Leptidea sinapis* is a scarce insect with about 90 sites in southern England and Wales. It used to be much more common and widespread in the 19th century but has declined drastically due to the decrease in coppicing. We are fortunate that it occurs in all our woodland sections especially where they have had a woodland block clear felled and there is a good supply of birdsfoot trefoil. It is a very delicate little butterfly with a slow and feeble flight, on the wing late May to June.

The White Admiral - *Ladoga camilla* is an insect of extensive woodland in southern England. Thin spindly growth of honeysuckle is required for breeding, preferably hanging in dappled light on ride edges. It overwinters as a larva wrapped in a leaf anchored to the stem by silk threads. It is a strong flyer with a distinctive flight pattern, three flaps and a glide, and is usually only seen in ones and twos as most of the time it is up in the canopy feeding on honeydew but it will come down to nectar in a sunny position.

A butterfly that was very scarce until a few years ago is the Brown Argus – *Aricia agestis* recorded for the first time in 1995 in Sane Copse and since then has been seen regularly in other sections but not in large numbers. The Holly Blue – *Celastrina argiolus* was not seen until 1990 in Sane Copse which coincided with a population increase all over East Anglia. It has been seen each year since and occurs in varying numbers. It is a double brooded insect, the larvae feeding on holly in the spring and ivy in the late summer.

Skippers have a good strong population throughout the sunny woodland rides and meadows. The Large – *Ochlodes venata*, Small – *Thymelicus sylvestris* and the Essex – *T. lineola* the latter being first recorded on the Estate in 1993. Our two scarce skippers are the dingy and the grizzled both preferring open, not too overgrown areas and where they have been recorded it has usually been on old railtrack sites; never plentiful and sometimes not being seen for a year or two. The Dingy – *Erynnis tages* was first recorded in 1991 and only spasmodically since. Its food plant is birdsfoot trefoil and the larvae feed on this plant exclusively. It lives alone in a tent of the food plant leaves spun up near the ground. A very quick flying butterfly, on the wing May to June, it perches with its wings outstretched but at night the wings are folded tent-wise like a moth.

The Grizzled – *Pyrgus mulvae* first recorded in 1984 and only occasionally seen since. Wild strawberry is its favourite food plant and like the dingy the larva is difficult to find as it draws the edge of a leaf around it holding it together with silk to form a tent. It is a very active butterfly with a swift darting flight and is on the wing May to June.

The Small Copper - *Lycaena phlaeas* has declined nationally due to intensification of agriculture it being more at home in flowery meadows than in woodland glades. It is however still quite common on the Estate and occurs in all of our sections and in good years with double or triple broods can be seen flying in May, July – August and September and sometimes in October. Broods are usually small and they are normally only seen flying in twos and threes. We have recorded the blue-spotted variety – *caeruleopunctata*.

One butterfly that certainly seems to be on the decline is the Wall – *Lasiommata megera*. This was once a common insect of rough ground and grassland and now is nationally very scarce. It has seldom been recorded on the Estate but it did make a brief comeback in 1991, unfortunately it has not been seen now for the past three years. The larva is a grass feeder in sunny places with no particular preference for a certain type of grass. We have the habitat, where is the butterfly?

The browns always give us a good showing with the Speckled Wood – *Pararge aegeria* being seen from May through to September being double and sometimes triple brooded. It is probably one of the last butterflies to be seen at the end of the season. It prefers shady woodland habitats or dappled sunlight in a leafy lane.

The Ringlet – *Aphantopus hyperantus* does well in our woodland rides and meadows as it favours very damp places and tall grasses. The numbers in each colony vary considerably and there are annual fluctuations, they seem to do better after a wet season. It is not a strong flyer and seems to hover over the grass heads. The flying season is short, July, when it can be seen feeding on bramble flowers. It overwinters as a larva in the base of grass clumps, sometimes feeding on a mild sunny day.

The Meadow Brown – *Maniola jurtina* can be seen flying from June to September in all our meadows and grassy rides. The larva is a grass feeder and will overwinter as a larva amongst thick grass. This makes it very vulnerable, with others, to winter flooding of grassland. The Gatekeeper or Hedge Brown – *Pyronia tithonus* is not seen on the wing for such a long period, July to August. This larva is also a grass feeder, feeding only at night. It also overwinters as a larva.

Butterflies are always best seen when the sun is up making them much more active and on a really hot day they move very fast indeed, photographers please note. Patches of flowering bramble, thistles and hemp agrimony growing in the sunlight are always good places to watch. Quite often you can come across a muddy patch in the sun and see them around the edge taking the salts in the mud, the whites are particularly fond of doing this. If you carefully observe where the butterfly is drinking it is possible, when it has flown off, to see its tongue imprints in the mud, usually in neat rows. One piece of kit that should always be carried is of course the hand net which comes in many shapes and sizes, some folding and some rigid, and is a matter of personal choice. Don't forget the notebook. Any specimens that are netted for observations should be released on the site as soon as notes have been made.

Moths

Moving on to the moths and starting with the macro's some of which can be seen flying during the daytime but the majority only fly at night. The day flying species are usually found in grassy habitats and can be seen as you disturb them when walking through the grass. Those seen most readily on sunny days are the ones that have conspicuous red markings on their wings, the burnets and the cinnabar. This bright red colouring is used as a warning to inform hungry birds that they are distasteful and probably poisonous. I say probably because of the art of mimicry amongst insects, black and yellow stripes and blotches being one of the many patterns used. The insect obtains its poisons by the larva feeding on poisonous plants, that is poisonous to other animals, and in so doing retains the toxins in its digestive system which would be harmful to any other creature that ate it.

A good example is the Cinnabar moth – *Hypocrita jacobaeae* which does not have a very strong flight as it has no need to avoid predatory birds. The large expanse of red on its wings denotes that is it poisonous having retained the toxins taken in by the larva when feeding on its poisonous food plant. The larva itself, with its conspicuous yellow and black stripes, feeds quite openly on ragwort and is avoided by birds the exception being the cuckoo who seems to be able to digest the toxins. It is also quite partial to hairy caterpillars as well which are usually avoided by most other birds.

The Burnets – *Zyganea sp.* both five and six spotted can often be seen on sunny days clustered, four to six of them, on knapweeds and thistle heads. These moths have black forewings with large red spots and the hind wings are red with a black border. The body fluids in these insects contain hydro-cyanic acids. They are on the wing May – August and can be quite common in meadows and grassy rides.

The clearwing moths are also day flyers, there are about 15 species but are seldom seen. They are called clearwings because they shed most of their wing scales on their first flight. This gives them the appearance of bees or wasps as they fly in the sun often with a hum or buzzing sound and when resting on vegetation they are easily mistaken for a wasp, bee or fly. Most of their bodies are banded black and yellow or orange and most have a tuft of hair at the tip of their abdomen. The larvae of this family eat into trees and roots sometimes spending up to three years inside as a larva, some can be spotted by frass coming from small holes.

Our biggest clearwing is the Hornet – *Sesia apiformis* with a body length of 25mm and a wing span of 45-50mm and the larva is found in poplar. The pencil sized exit holes of this moth can be found around the base of the tree, often with a pupal case protruding from it, although these are soon blown away by the wind. They are not considered a pest as their tunnelling does not affect the tree growth and they do not extend up the trunk more than 20-25cm from the ground level. The larva in its final stages will make an exit hole and then seal it before retreating back a bit to pupate. The spiky pupa then breaks through this membrane in July, unless it has already been found by a

JAN FEB MAR APR MAY JUN JUL AUG SEP OCT NOV DEC

BUTTERFLIES ON THE WING

Black hairstreak (Strymonidia pruni)
Brimstone (Gonepteryx rhamni)
Comma (Polygonia c-album)
Common blue (Polyommatus icarus)
Dingy skipper (Erynnis tages)
Gatekeeper (Pyronia tithonus)
Green-veined white (Pieris napi)
Grizzled skipper (Pyrgus malvae)
Holly blue (Celastrina argiolus)
Large skipper (Ochlodes venata)
Large white (Pieris brassicae)
Marbled white (Melanargia galanthea)
Meadow brown (Maniola jurtina)
Orange tip (Anthocharis cardamines)
Painted lady (Vanessa cardui)
Peacock (Inachis io)
Purple hairstreak (Quercusia quercus)
Red admiral (Vanessa atalanta)
Ringlet (Aphantopus hyperantus)
Small copper (Lycaena phlaeas)
Small heath (Coenonympha pamphilus)
Small skipper (Thymelicus sylvestris)
Small tortoiseshell (Aglais urticae)
Small white (Pieris rapae)
Speckled wood (Pararge aegeria)
Wall brown (Lasiommata megera)
White admiral (Ladoga camilla)
Wood white (Leptidea sinapis)

woodpecker which is expert at locating these membrane covered holes and extracting the pupa. The emergent moth will sit and dry out on the trunk before crawling up the tree to find a sunny patch and eventual flight which takes a time of two to three hours. Because of its hornet-like camouflage and swift flight it is seldom seen unless found resting on a tree or leaf. Several of our blocks of poplar do have colonies of this moth and for photographic purposes we searched one block in 1996. Those of us with less knowledge of this insect's habits were told to look on the trunks of the poplars up to about shoulder height. After 20 minutes with everyone diligently searching one of those with the 'lesser knowledge' said "Is that what you want up there?" pointing to a couple of moths about four metres up the tree. All eyes turned upwards to reveal not one but a mating pair! How do we photograph them up there? Can you picture the scene, two elderly gentlemen leaning with their backs against the tree supporting another elderly gentleman on their shoulders who was carefully boxing the mating pair. After a few cries of "hurry up" from those down below, the operation was successful and the pair were brought down and placed back on the tree in a sunny spot at eye level where they were duly photographed, still paired!

The other slightly smaller hornet clearwing is the Lunar Hornet – *S. bembeciformis* which has the same life history but uses sallow as its host.

There are several other of the smaller clearwings recorded on the Estate and all using other host plants. They can all be mistaken for flies or bees when seen on the wing.

One of the earliest and probably most often seen day flying moths from May to August is the Green Oak Tortrix – *T. viridana*, if not the moth then its larvae hanging on threads from oak trees. This moth can sometimes reach plague proportions, it can and often does cause severe defoliation of oaks. The moth, a weak flyer, is small and pale green and can sometimes be seen festooning the trunks of oak trees.

One large moth that may be seen during the day is the Emperor – *Saturnia pavonia*. It is only the male that flies during the day, usually in the afternoon, seeking out the female who is advertising her presence by emitting a pheremone scent which can be detected by the male up to 2km away. The background wing colour of both male and female is orange/brown with prominent eye spots on both fore and hind wings. The larva is a very striking creature and can be found May to July. Although starting off brown in colour when young, it soon develops into a bright green livery with gold, sometimes pink, spots in bands round the body and attains a length of 55mm. In spite of its bright colour and size it is seldom seen when poking about amongst the bramble which would be its main foodplant on the Estate.

The plume moths are an interesting group and whilst not usually actively flying through the day are often disturbed as you walk through the vegetation. These moths are unique in that they have their wings divided, having two lobes in the forewing and three in the hindwing, giving the appearance of a plumed fan when open. The many plumed, *Alucita hexadactyla*, in a separate family, has each wing divided into six lobes. They are often observed resting on vegetation because of their angled resting position. Due to their wing formation, the plumes will roll up on each other and are held at right angles to the body, showing them up as a slender T shape, they are usually white or fawn coloured.

One that did give us an interesting time was *Porritia galactodactyla* which we investigated in 1997-98. It started quite casually with a chance remark from David that he had just found the larvae on greater burdock, the only known foodplant for this moth, to which my reply was "that plant doesn't grow on the Estate".

I recalled photographing this moth in 1982 but I knew that we did not have greater burdock growing anywhere on the Estate and that was how the investigation started. The end result of this study was to display specimens and photos at the British Entomological and Natural History Society in Kensington. The paper accompanying this exhibit is given below:

Arctium minus ssp minus
(Lesser Burdock)
a new food plant for
Porittia galactodactyla (D. & S.)

The only known foodplant in Britain for this moth is *Arctium lappa* (Greater Burdock). In Europe, the range of this moth is restricted to the distribution of *Arctium lappa*. (Gielis (1996) – Microlepidoptera of Europe, Vol 1 – Pterphoridae). In May 1993 larvae were recorded at Sane Copse (SP852541) in Yardley Chase, Northamptonshire (VC 32). This colony still existed in 1998, in an area no more than 100 metres radius. JAR recalled photographing similar larval feeding on burdock in 1982 along an abandoned railway line adjacent to Barnstaple Wood (SP850525), also in Yardley Chase, this site being in Bucks (VC 24). The site was revisited in 1998 and the colony was still present, again in a very restricted area no more than 100 metres radius. These two sites are about a mile apart. They are in an area of mixed woodland several thousand acres in extent, where *Arctium minus* is abundant, but *Arctium lappa* is absent. No other colonies have been detected, after searching extensively for the past five years.

The failure of these colonies to expand over periods of five and sixteen years respectively may indicate a reluctance or inability of the moth to disperse, although surrounded by apparently suitable habitat.

Only during 1998 did we question whether we were looking on the wrong host-plant, and collected leaf specimens with larval feeding in May and again in August, together with flower heads to enable our County Recorder to check which plant is host to these larvae. All plants on which we found larval feeding are confirmed as *Arctium minus ssp minus*.

The exhibit shows autumn and spring feeding of the larva *Porittia galactodactyla* on *Arctium minus ssp minus*, a newly recorded host plant.

D V Manning and J A Richardson.

To find moths in the daylight they do not necessarily have to be flying about, they are there in the form of larvae and while most are found singly there are those that are more readily seen. These are the ones that lead a communal life, at least at the start of their lives. They spin webs over leaves and branches forming a conspicuous tent to which they retreat during the night or adverse weather conditions. On warm sunny days they will come out to feed, sometimes in ones and twos, sometimes en masse. Some, as they grow bigger, will leave the tent altogether but will continue to feed gregariously. One typical web spinner is the Lackey – *Malacosoma neustria* which spends most of its larval life in the confines of the tent which is usually spun over a patch of leaves. It is a very large larva compared with the size of the adult moth.

The Small Eggar – *Eriogaster lanestris* which was very scarce over southern England a few years back made a good comeback in 1990 with several webs being recorded on hawthorn in the eastern woods, seven webs in all. The larvae continue to use the tent until they descend to the bottom of the hedge to pupate on branches or in debris and will sometimes spend two to three years as a pupa before emerging as an adult. We are still finding the occasional larval tent today.

The Buff-tip – *Phalera bucephala*, the larvae whilst not spinning a web do feed communally when young but eventually go their own way. They can usually still be located easily by observing a completely defoliated branch, usually a young tree, and on examination 20-30 larvae can be seen along the branch and twigs. When that branch is devoid of leaves they will all mostly move on to another. The adult moth has buff coloured tips to its wings with its thorax and head being the same buff colour. When resting on a branch this gives the impression of a broken twig.

There are many other, often smaller, moths that can be seen flying on a sunny day, often moving very quickly and these need to be netted for positive identification. Some of these will be micro-moths which I will talk about later.

The vast majority of moths will be recorded by running a moth light at night and this operation is much dependent upon the weather. Apart from it actually raining, which completely stops play for the moth catchers, the phases of the moon and the wind strength can greatly affect the numbers of moths that will come to the light.

The main lamp that is used is run from a generator which, due to its weight, needs to be transported by a vehicle. Wheelbarrows can be used but it is better with an engine and this does restrict the area of woodland that can be recorded. Over the past years the FC and the MoD have laid some stone roads which has enabled us to extend the range of our mothing nights further into the wood than we could in the 1980s. Apart from the main mercury vapour lamp run from the generator there are also usually one or two Actinic lamps which operate from 12v car batteries, these are put out in adjacent rides away from the main lamp. The set up routine is fairly standard and follows the same pattern on most nights. Arrive about an hour before light up time and select a suitable patch – level with no bramble trip wires and not too near ditches. Spread out the white sheet and bang in the stake, attach lamp to stake and site generator a reasonable distance away, check haversack for specimen boxes, flask and sandwiches and most important a torch. The next job is to put out any other battery operated lamps and do the 'duskings' that is to wander down the ride with a hand net to catch the early flyers, chat about the nights possibilities and listen to the woodcock roding overhead.

This is also the time to do any sugaring, that is to coat small patches of tree trunks or fence posts, using a paint brush, with a home concocted brew of 'treacle'. The recipe for this mixture varies from person to person, each having their own secret ingredient but the basic formula is:-

1lb black treacle	2lb brown sugar
½ pint beer	2 tots of rum

(apologies to any euro-regulated bodies)

Boil these ingredients in an old saucepan (check with the wife first) and stir into a uniform mixture, the longer it is boiled, the stickier it gets. During the night a nominated person should walk around and visit all the coated patches, with his torch, to see what has alighted around the edge of the patch of sugar. This method of recording works best on a warm humid night, windy nights should be avoided. This sticky mixture is not intended to fix insects to the tree or post but to encourage them to sup from it and they can sometimes appear quite drunk. Any specimens that are wanted can be gently boxed for identification later. It won't only be moths that take advantage of this free meal but earwigs, flies, wasps and even the odd beetle.

Back to the main lamp, contact, and we have lift off or should it be fly down! Some nights can produce moths right away whilst others can give you quite a wait. Some are caught with the hand net as they fly in, others settle on the sheet waiting to be identified. Watch out for the black and yellow striped jobs that buzz, hornets can sometimes be a problem especially when you go back to check the catches in the Actinic lamps later on. The different species of moths seem to arrive in waves, two or three nets being wielded with a good strong wrist action, back hand stroke being favoured and then a quiet period before the arrival of the next wave. Sometimes an odd wing or two will drift down and you then know that you have bats overhead. If you should have a prolonged quiet period there is one sure way to bring them flying in and that is to get out your camp stool, sit down and pour out a cup of coffee. It works every time!

Sometimes when all this is going on I take my torch and wander off down a ride to see what can be found on the edge vegetation, there are a lot of larvae that feed at night. In June/July it is very pleasant to see any glow-worms that might be about, the females up in the grass glowing to attract the males. Sometimes you can catch a fox in the torch beam and stare it out for a minute before he/she breaks away. When you return to the main lamp the others are always keen to tell you about the really good specimen of an uncommon moth that flew in while you were away.

Depending on how varied the surrounding woodland is will affect the variety of moths and other insects that will fly in. The sheet is often visited by beetles, caddis flies, water boatmen, craneflies, mosquitos (they usually prefer you to the sheet) and many others. To build a proper picture of the local species in the area you need, if possible, to run a light at the same spot each month for a number of years.

The object of these mothing nights is to identify the various species that fly in. They should not be used for the purpose of taking or killing any insect. It is sometimes necessary to take specimens home for positive identification and this does sometimes entail the killing of these specimens. The method sometimes employed, of boxing everything that comes in to the light, and this could easily be in the hundreds, for 'sorting out' at home is not a good method of study and should not be practised. These nights should always be attended by at least one person who is capable of identifying the majority of the moths as they fly in. Your first experience in working with a moth light is very enjoyable as it is the opportunity to see an insect first hand that would probably not be seen at any other time, except perhaps only as an illustration in a reference book. It sometimes seems strange that insects that fly during the night have such delightful colour and patterns. Who is intended to see them? Most of the patterning does provide good camouflage during the daytime when they are at rest on a tree trunk or vegetation but the sometimes iridescent colours can only be seen when flying in to the light.

The number of species, some 800 plus, available to be caught are too numerous to discuss in detail. I think that the hawkmoths are always immediately noticed when flying in to the light due mainly to their size, all in the region of 80-100mm wing span. They are all quite colourful especially when the hind wings and body are exposed and on the Estate we have recorded eight different species. The larvae of hawkmoths are all large, 60-100mm in length and all of them have a short tail or horn on their rear end.

Last but certainly not least we should mention the micro-moths. This group of mostly very small moths tend to be neglected because they are not so easily identified or even seen. They do sometimes fly by day but due to their size are often missed. They also fly in to the moth light but again are often disregarded. It is fair to say that when we were joined by David in 1993 there was a lot of interest generated in these micro-moths. To most of us they stopped being flying things and became instead squiggles and blotches on leaves, reasonably easy to find and they don't fly away. Leaf-mines, those squiggles and windows that can be found on the leaves of all types of plant are the larval homes of these small moths. A mine in a leaf does not mean that you have found a moth as other species also create mines, such as flies, mites and beetles. The interest generated within our group initially as we all started finding mines for David to identify generated a phrase often heard when walking along a track, "it's a b----- fly", but we did get better at it. These moths mostly have only one host foodplant and each species has its own shape and position on the leaf of its mine or window. This enables you to first find the foodplant and then look for the mine. Where more than one species shares the same foodplant then the mine shape and position will enable you to tell A from B. In the case of scarce or seldom recorded species it is very useful to have several pairs of eyes looking and often quite successfully. Over the past seven years all this diligent searching has enabled David to record 22 new county records and has certainly increased our awareness of the life habits of this interesting group of moths. Shortage of available literature on this group could be a problem for anyone wishing to take up the study of these small moths.

Finally I can only say that moths can be a fascinating study right from the egg to the flying insect. Shapes and colours of both larva and moth are limitless. In the larval stage some have only one specific host plant while others will eat any one of half a dozen plants, most are solitary, others gregarious and some cannibalistic. In flight some are strong and fly great distances, others are weak and stay in a very small area. Wingspans range from 7-120mm and some females are wingless. There is one that squeaks when handled, the Deaths Head – *Acherontia atropos* which unfortunately has not yet been recorded on the Estate.

As a general study or by selecting a specific group it can be a very worthwhile occupation and they can be found every month of the year. Books to aid identification are numerous and range greatly in price and usefulness. Don't buy the first one that you see; shop around and ask advice from other naturalists.

Hymenoptera

One group of insects that are always about, especially on warm sunny days, are the bees and wasps (*Hymenoptera*). The Hornet – *Vespa crabro* is a large insect up to 35mm in length and flying very swiftly. It is widespread throughout England and Wales but local, often quite common where it does occur. Locally it has increased greatly in numbers since the 1980s and is now being recorded in all sections and nests are frequently being found. Apart from hollow trees they are fond of nesting in other odd or awkward places. The ranger's highseats placed throughout the woodlands are a favourite place. High up and dry they are not easy to remove when the seat is required for use and you don't always see them until you have climbed the ladder. One awkward nest for me in 1997 was built in the doorway of the conservation lodge, a brick building left by the army. The nest was attached to the concrete lintel above the doorway and was about the size of a rugby ball. Needless to say we had not used the lodge for some weeks. On that particular day I opened the door to put some kit away and was aware of a buzzing sound in my right ear, a quick glance upwards confirmed what I thought and that was followed by an even quicker exit. Shutting the door quickly behind me I realised that the top of my head had only missed touching the nest by about an inch. Regretfully the only way that I could get over this problem was to burn out the nest. I do like hornets and find them much less aggressive than wasps. They will allow you to investigate them quite closely as long as you don't disturb them. This time, unfortunately, they had to go.

The Common and German Wasps – *Vespula sp.* are generally bad tempered insects and are plentiful everywhere although the annual numbers fluctuate greatly. Some years nests can be seen everywhere, in trees, hanging from the eaves of bunkers and in the ground. Most nests are constructed in the ground, usually in banks and old tree roots, starting with a disused vole or mouse hole which is then enlarged by the wasps to about 20-30cm. A nest of this size could house up to

3.000 brood cells. The badger finds a lot of these ground nests and digs them out for the grubs inside. All that is left when he has finished with it are a few fragments of the nest and one or two confused late returning wasps. In towns and around buildings they favour lofts and cavity walls and these nests can be very large as there is usually other support for these fragile structures. It is unusual to see nests free hanging unless there is a population explosion as happened in 1995. We saw nests hanging from the canopies of the bunkers and in the branches of trees, nearly all of these were predated over a period of about three weeks in July and August, probably by woodpeckers. Once the nest is formed by the original team of workers and the cells completed, the nest itself doesn't usually increase in size. About midsummer the nest is a very busy place with extensions to the old combs and the building of some new cells. These are required to meet the continual supply of eggs generated by the Queen. To meet these constant demands the old cells are cleaned out and used again, most cells in a nest will have been used twice and perhaps three times. The cleaning out of the cells is not done by the wasps but by the larvae of a Drone-fly – *Volucella inanis* which are ever present in the nest and are accepted by the wasps. Wasps also sometimes nest in the high-seats but are usually hidden away in a sheltered corner or under a chair. There was such a chair in a high-seat in 1999. We all knew about it but during one weekend this particular wood was visited by a group of travellers who had organised a 'rave'. It was dark and camp fires were lit. Someone decided to go aloft (for the view?) and sat on the chair, I bet that was the hottest rave that he/she had ever been to!

Although wasps like sweet things, the food they provide for their larvae is pre-masticated animal matter, usually flies, so they are beneficial in controlling some insect pests. They don't serve any useful purpose generally in the pollination of crops.

The Honey Bee – *Apis melifera* is occasionally found in the wild, usually seen as a migrating swarm, but sometimes a wild colony is found in a hollow tree. A nest in this situation can become very large as it can remain at this site for several years, being added to each year. Sometimes a comb will be started in the open hanging from a branch, usually as a result of a swarm settling, but these seldom last as they are open to the weather and predation. One infamous colony that was situated in an old oak tree on the corner of a ride in Barnstable Wood was there for five or six years and they were a very aggressive colony. If you walked past the tree in the summer you regularly got buzzed and while I personally never got stung (some near misses though) there have been others of us who have been stung, even after being warned. This colony has now died out and the tree was taken over by hornets.

The demise of this well established colony has probably been caused by the recently arrived mite *Varroa jacobsoni*. This mite, which arrived from the continent in 1992, has devastated bee colonies in England and Wales and has now reached the west Scottish borders and Ireland. Whilst we can maintain some control over the effects of this mite in hive bees, wild bee colonies could soon be wiped out due to the overall effect of this mite killing some and weakening the remainder making them more susceptible to other pests and diseases.

Bumblebees – *Bombus sp.* are large hairy insects which can be seen flying on warm sunny days, some as early as April, seeking out any available nectar. Only mated Queens survive the winter to start new colonies in the spring. They form annual colonies, quite often in old mouse holes and sometimes in the base of large tussocks of grass. The nest itself is usually a ball constructed with grass and moss. The numbers of these insects seem to be decreasing over the past five to six years and they are increasingly under threat from intensive use of the land. They require a constant source of pollen and nectar to keep the brood going. Although these colonies are not as large as honey bees they can contain several hundred workers at their peak time. There are 28 species of Bombus and they are all very important for crop pollination.

The Leaf-cutter Bee – *Megachile centuncularis* is in the group of carpenter bees (*Xylocopa*) and is a very interesting and skilled bee. Its nest is made up of small tubes constructed from pieces of leaf, usually rose, which are built in a tunnel excavated in decaying wood and quite often several tunnels side by side. Each cell is made up of about twelve pieces of leaf which have been accurately cut by the bee, circular pieces for the base and top and ovate pieces for the wall. It is a small bee about 10mm long and often goes unnoticed when flying unless it is carrying a piece of cut leaf in June and July. When a cell has been built the bee will fill it with a mixture of pollen and honey and will lay an egg on the surface, the cell is then capped off and work commences on the next cell in line. The eggs hatch and eventually produce a full grown bee which then waits for several weeks until it senses the weather conditions are right and then cuts its way out of its cell. The bottom cell, although laid first, has to wait until its neighbours have vacated their cells before emerging into the daylight.

One other wasp-like insect that can be encountered on a sunny day is the Wood Wasp or Horntail – *Urocerus gigas*, in spite of its colouring it is not a true wasp but a sawfly. Normally found in pine woods between May and October, it is very large with a black and yellow body 30mm long and a tail of 10-12mm, its wing span is 55mm. The fearsome looking tail is in fact a shield for its ovipositor which is used to drill eggs into the wood of sickly or felled pine trees where the larva will spend two to three years before emerging as a full grown fly. They fly actively on sunny days with a loud buzzing sound. The males are smaller and of course they have no ovipositor. This insect does not sting and is completely harmless to us. The sawflies are an interesting group of insects, most of them brightly coloured with sizes ranging from 7-14mm. They all use the same method of breeding where the female drills or saws a hole in a stem, leaf or root and deposits an egg. The ovipositors of these smaller sawflies are not always visible as they are mostly tucked beneath the body.

Galls

A number of *Hymenopterous* species are tiny parasitic wasps which lay eggs on other insect larvae, sometimes attached to the outer skin or inserted into the body. Others deposit eggs in or on plant tissue which nearly all induce a gall formation, especially on oak.

Galls are something I am sure we have all seen when walking through the fields and woodland. They are an abnormal growth or swelling produced by a plant as a result of an attack by an insect when laying its eggs, they can also be caused by a fungal infection. They come in all shapes and sizes and some have their own colouration.

Most of the galls are caused by mites and insects, the flies and cynipid wasps amongst them produce some very elaborate structures. Most galls will only grow if the eggs hatch and will continue to grow until the larvae either die or pupate. After that it will retain its shape until the leaf or fruit drops off, only sometimes changing to autumnal colours before falling.

The oak must be the best place to guarantee seeing galls of various kinds. The shape of each gall is specific to the creature that laid the egg, thus you can identify the creature by recognising the gall. Most trees and some plants will have an insect that selects it as a host plant, usually on the leaves in the case of trees and stems in plants although there is no hard and fast rule to this. Returning to the oak which is host to at least 40 different gall producing creatures the most familiar of which must be the oak apple for size and the various spangle galls for numbers. The general shape and colours can be numerous but most are spherical or ovoid, some with hairs or spines. I think the one with the most complicated shape is a recent arrival in the country, the Knopper Gall – *Andricus quercuscalisis*, introduced from France in the early 1960s and it is rapidly spreading northwards. The knopper galls that occur on our common oaks, the pedunculate and the sessile, only produce female wasps. It is the turkey oak that produces both male and female wasps. The moral seems to be that if you don't want this gall, don't plant turkey oak near our two native oaks.

The sticky wrinkly/walnut shaped gall grows from inside the acorn cup and can eventually cover the acorn completely, sometimes two or three galls will form around one acorn. I don't know whether infected acorns will germinate into trees – it possibly depends on how severe the growth is.

The spangle galls are flat discs about 5mm diameter and the underside of a leaf can sometimes be covered with 80-100 of these galls. There are four species, all cynipid wasps *Neurotus quercus-baccarum, N. numismalis, N. tricolor* and *N. albipes.* These galls fall to the ground in the autumn and the larva continues to develop inside them getting winter protection from the covering of the fallen leaves. Female wasps emerge from them in the spring.

Another very common and easily seen gall grows on the field and dog rose, the Bedeguar Gall or Robins Pincushion – *Diplolepis rosae.* The eggs are laid in the unopened buds which causes a round growth covered with a mass of filaments, green at first and changing through to red in the autumn. They can vary in sizes ranging from 2-10cm and can contain up to 60 larval chambers.

For those who like to pick blackberries you can often come across a lumpy cylindrical swelling on a stem, turning red/purple in the autumn with any of last year's galls showing up as a light coloured sponge, very hard, full of exit holes. This is the work of a cynipid wasp *Lasioptera rubi.*

Galls on low growing plants are not so easily seen but one type that often stands out is the fasciation of a plant. This is where the stem of a plant develops a broad flattened appearance usually on the main stem sometimes appearing to fuse three or four stems together. This formation usually appears on tall plants like thistles, spurges, plantains, dandelions and others. It can sometimes fuse flower heads together and these make interesting photo subjects as they will continue to bloom. Fasciation is not always caused by an insect attack but could be due to a fungal infection or even an internal viral infection.

Apart from disfiguration, gall growth does not appear to adversely affect the well being of the host plant as it is often seen that a densely galled plant will continue to reproduce freely.

Bugs

Although people who study insects are often called bug-hunters or "bugsy" it is only one order of insect which is truly a bug . This order is the Hemiptera, consisting of insects which do not have biting jaws but have a piercing beak (the rostrum) which is used to suck the juices mainly from plants but also from other animals. Most of them have wings but some are wingless, they are a fairly colourful group and vary a great deal in size and shape.

The ones that are probably the most noticeable, usually on trees and shrubs, are the shield bugs, they are quite colourful and their bodies are generally shield shaped. Some can emit pungent fluids when disturbed and many hibernate over the winter as adults when their body colours will change to autumnal browns. Their sizes range from 5-15mm.

Ground bugs and stilt bugs are very numerous and usually sombre coloured but some do have bright red warning colours. These bugs, found mostly in the grasses and lower vegetation and in the ground litter, could sometimes be confused with beetles. Mirid bugs are the largest family and are found crawling over the lower herbage on quite long thin legs. They are generally more colourful and are mostly herbivores and many of them pass the winter as eggs.

The 'hoppers' are very numerous, being generally divided into three groups; tree, frog and plant hoppers. The Tree Hopper – *Centrotus cornutus* although dark coloured, nearly black, and small, up to 10mm, has quite a striking appearance with its pronotum extending back over the body and with two 'horns' protruding, one each side, giving it the appearance of a buffalo when viewed head on. It likes woodland habitats and is an active jumper.

Froghoppers are generally various shades of brown and all very similar in shape and size and always jump at the first signs of disturbance, the nymphs of most of these live in a mass of froth generated by the nymph to prevent dehydration.

The largest and most colourful of these froghoppers is *Cercopis vulnerata* and can be spotted quite easily due to is distinctive black and red markings and is very common and found throughout the Estate on the lower vegetation.

Leafhoppers are very similar to the froghoppers but are generally more colourful and larger with the hind legs being more spiny.

The last insects to be mentioned from this order are the aquatic species, some living on the water surface film and margins whilst others are submerged. The most noticeable when coming upon a pond or ditch are the boatmen, *Notenecta* and *Corixa sp.* actively swimming or rapidly diving when they first see your shadow on the water surface. The other smaller surface dwellers are Pond Skaters – *Gerris sp.* Water Measurer – *Hydrometra stagnorum* and Water Cricket – *Velia currens*. To me the most interesting pond bugs are the Water Scorpion – *Nepa cinerea* and the Water Stick Insect or Long Water Scorpion – *Ranatra linearis*. Both of these creatures crawl slowly amongst the submerged pond weed at the edge of the pond, always resting with their breathing tube piercing the surface film and waiting for their food to come within striking distance of their raptorial front legs. *N. cinerea* is flat bodied and dark brown, 17-22mm long (excluding the breathing tube) and it cannot fly as its wing muscles are atrophied. In spite of this if you lift the wings the body underneath is a striking orange/red. Is this inherent from the days when it was able to fly? *R. linearis* is a light tan colour and has a thin cylindrical body 30-34mm long (excluding the breathing tube). All these aquatic species are carnivores except for one or two *corixids*.

Dragonflies

Whilst still in the vicinity of water now would seem a good time to mention our dragonfly and damselfly family (Odonata) which are probably one of the best colonies in Northamptonshire producing 20 species to date out of a list of 45. The last one to be added to our list was the Hairy Hawker – *Brachytron pratense*. First recorded in Sane Copse in 1998, this dragonfly is extending its northern range and has been reported from one or two sites in Northamptonshire and it is now breeding in some of our ponds in the Chase. One species that has decreased in numbers over the past years is the Broad Bodied Chaser – *Libellula depressa*. This dragonfly prefers young open ponds and is usually one of the first to colonise a new pond. This could well be the reason for its decline in numbers as our ponds have developed a good thick scrub surround over these past years but it will probably continue to hold on as we carry on with the pond edge clearance plan.

Although dragonflies need water for breeding purposes they can and do travel long distances from their pond once mating and egg laying is completed. The big hawkers especially can often be seen flying in groups of a dozen or more over a swarm of flies with no ponds in sight. In the days of horse power they were often seen flying over a herd of horses in a field catching the flies that were ever present. This gave them the Victorian name of 'horse stingers' when in fact they were doing the horses a favour.

All these insects are brightly coloured and a joy to see on a sunny day and even better if you can find one that is resting with its wings reflecting the sun. They seem to have their own personal perches around the pond. Unfortunately this part of their lives is short lived.

Most of their life, two to three years, is spent as a nymph in the depths of the pond. They crawl and lurk in the pond weed or on the bottom waiting for their prey, which can be as large as a stickleback, to come within striking distance. The lower lip (labium) of the nymph is modified into a very successful grasping mechanism, flicking out at great speed to seize its meal as it passes by. Whilst not able to swim as such, it is capable of swift movement. When danger threatens it will contract its body forcing a jet of water from its tail-end which will rapidly propel it some 8-10cm.

When the adult is ready to emerge the nymph will crawl from the pond, early in the morning, onto the reeds or grass or sometimes a small tree which can be some distance from the water. Here it will hang for a while before splitting its skin above the thorax and allowing the dragonfly to withdraw its body and wings. These empty cases (exuvia) can often be found attached to pondside vegetation where the white tracheal sacs are clearly visible.

Beetles

Beetles (*Coleoptera*) are the most numerous species in the world with about 4,000 occurring in Britain. They are a very diverse group and can be found in almost every situation. The largest British beetle (not recorded in Northamptonshire) is the Stag Beetle – *Lucarnus cervus* the male being up to 55mm long with some of the smaller species being a mere 2mm . Most of them are sombre coloured blacks and browns but there are a number of brightly coloured species with green, red and yellow paternations. Weevils are included in this group, the rather dumpy ones with a long rostrum at the front.

Most of them are terrestrial but there are twelve separate families that are aquatic, probably the best known family amongst these being the *Dytiscidae*. This family contains one of our largest water beetles, the Great Diving Beetle – *Dytiscus marginalis* an olive brown colour with yellow margins to its wing case. It is carnivorous with a healthy appetite and with its size of 33mm can tackle quite large prey. The larva, which is sometimes called the water tiger is also very voracious and attains a length of 40mm eating anything up to its own size.

All water beetles can and do fly, some being more active than others, but this one is a strong flyer (usually at night) and can spread easily from pond to pond.

The Whirligig Beetle – *Gyrinus*, of which there are ten species, is the one most easily spotted when approaching a pond. Its is a small shiny black beetle seen in groups of 12-80 plus swimming rapidly round in circles on the water surface. The eyes are divided for above and below vision. This gives them extremely good eyesight both from above and below and if you were to plunge a net into the middle of such a group you would be lucky to catch more than six or seven. They would have dived before the net hit the water. Another interesting water-beetle is the Screech Beetle – *Hygrobia tarda*, this will only be seen when caught with a net. It has a strongly convex body about 15mm long, reddish brown in colour with blackish elytra (wing covers). When it is held gently between finger and thumb it will emit a squeak by rubbing the tip of its abdomen against its wing covers.

In a large forest area such as the Chase a substantial number of species of the longhorn group (*Cerambycidae*) can be found. The larvae of these species are predominantly wood feeders, some boring into sound wood whilst most will prefer soft rotting wood and these can spend as much as three years as larvae. One of our largest longhorns is *Stenocorus meridianus* ranging in size from 15 to 25mm and with very variable colourations. The larvae feed on various deciduous trees and the adult, as with most of this group, can be found feeding on pollen or basking in the sun from May to June.

A closely related species is *Rhagium mordax* up to 22mm long, and it can often be seen basking in the sun from May to August. The larvae prefer oak and can be found in or on rotting stumps.

One handsome beetle, easily seen resting or feeding on flowers on sunny days is *Strangalia maculata* a yellow, black spotted longhorn up to 20mm long. It is our most common longhorn in the woods and on ride edges and it favours the white inflorescences of umbellifera plants and roses. The larvae feed on old tree stumps of oak and birch.

There is one other very attractive longhorn which is probably on the extreme of its northern range and not very common elsewhere in the south. It is *Agapanthia villosoviridescens*, up to 22mm long. It can be found from June to September on various plants, mainly thistles, which act as its larval host, and has been recorded in all of our woodland sections.

One very useful group of beetles are the *Silphidae*, burying beetles, sometimes known as sexton beetles. There are 20 species occurring in the British Isles, some very common and there are seven species recorded on the Estate. Two are all black, one pale orange with spots and the rest are red with black bars. In spite of their name they don't all bury the body but those that do are very efficient at it. They do their work unobtrusively and are usually only seen when you disturb a small corpse. Once they have located a small body, usually by smell, they work very quickly, tunnelling under the corpse and dragging it down as they go, some will skin the body as they go. They mostly work in pairs but there are sometimes more, depending on the size of the body. A group of three to five beetles can bury a mole in a few hours to a depth of several centimetres. Once the body is buried , eggs are laid on or near the corpse, sometimes in excavated galleries running off. Their efforts are one of the reasons that small bodies are seldom found in the countryside unless recently killed. On a hard road surface magpies and crows will take over the disposal duties.

Our two Cardinal beetles *Pyrchroides sp.* are the red or scarlet beetles, 9 –18mm long. They are often seen in May and June resting on vegetation along the woodland edge and in hedgerows. Their larvae live under the bark of dead deciduous trees.

The *Coccinellidae* family, commonly known as ladybirds, are a very well known and popular group of beetles. They are small brightly coloured beetles and are seen everywhere. Their general colours are red or yellow patterned in black and in some the patterns can vary considerably, especially the Two Spot – *Adalia bipunctata*. Both the larvae and the adults are carnivorous and are very beneficial in the control of aphids and other garden pests. Of the 24 British species there are four that are not carnivorous and they live mainly on mildews.

All our ladybirds hibernate during the winter period, often selecting their site in September or early October, each species showing a preference for a certain type of habitat. The largest number that I have ever found together on one site, although not on this Estate, was 320 under tree bark.

One, to me, amusing group are the click beetles (*Elateridae*) a large family of 70 species. Their elongated bodies are in various shades of brown and are 8-17mm long. They are wood and vegetable feeders and can sometimes be a serious pest to horticulture and agriculture. They are good flyers and love basking in the sun. Their name 'click' derives from the fact that they can right themselves when falling on their back. They are able to arch their back causing a tension between the pro and meso-thorax which causes the edges to catch and force the base of the elytra to strike the ground with sufficient power to flip the beetle over in a backwards somersault producing a distinct clicking sound in the process.

Last but not least of our beetle population is the Glow-worm – *Lampyris noctiluca*, a now very scarce beetle of southern England. We are fortunate to have several small colonies in most of our woodland sections.

The male, up to 12mm long, is a dull black/brown colour with large eyes, he flies at night seeking out the luminous light emitted by the wingless female. She is bigger than the male, up to 20mm, and in June and July will climb up grass tufts at night where she will emit her light from the underside of the hind end of her abdomen which she can switch on and off at will. The larvae, which look very much like the female, are carnivorous and feed on snails. During the day these beetles can sometimes be found under logs, always in damp conditions.

There is a little ditty that springs to mind here which always brings a smile to my face –

> I wish I was a glow-worm,
> A glow-worm's never glum,
> 'cos how can you be grumpy
> When the sun shines out your bum!

Orthoptera

Grasshoppers and crickets, of which there are 38 British species, are a generally chirpy little bunch and quite colourful. Their song is produced by rubbing a set of stridulating pegs situated, usually, on the hind femur against a stiff ridge on their wing case. The song produced by the male is to attract the females and is specific to that species, some song is quiet with little more than a hiss, others are loud and can be heard some distance away. Females also stridulate but produce a much weaker sound. A sunny day in a large meadow can sometimes be quite musical. The Estate does not have much old undisturbed meadowland and this could be one of the reasons why we have only recorded five species including two groundhoppers.

We also have three bush crickets in our woods. These are the ones with the long antennae, longer than their bodies, and are usually found on shrubs and trees. Their ovipositors are much larger than the grasshoppers and look rather like a scimitar blade. The Speckled – *Leptophyes punctatissima* and the Oak – *Meconema thalassinum* Bush crickets are green coloured tree dwellers and are most active at night. Our other bush cricket the Dark – *Pholidoptera griseoaptera* is mainly a low bush dweller and is active on sunny days.

To finish with the insects I can only say that there is much work still to be done on the less familiar orders —lacewings, scorpion flies and earwigs etc. This last one *Forficula auricularia* is one of the very few insects that brood their eggs – they really do make good mothers! Laid in an excavated chamber in the ground or under a stone (30-50 eggs) in early spring, the female will stay sealed up with them, turning and washing the eggs to prevent mildew forming on them. When they hatch, around April to May, she will stay with the young nymphs up to their first instar and beyond, keeping intruders away from the nest hole including the male earwig as he is not impartial to a young nymph for breakfast.

The remainder of our small creatures do not come within the generally accepted insect groups. Crustaceans such as woodlice, centipedes and millipedes, all favouring damp conditions under logs and stones. Harvestmen are an active group running about freely over both meadow and woodland, these chaps have the ability to replace one of their limbs should it be lost in action.

Arachnida

The very last group of small creatures, all eight legged, are the Arachnida (Spiders) which also includes mites. Not everybody's choice of pet but fascinating none the less.

They are another very under recorded group and are often disliked by people who see them running about indoors. There seems to be an inbuilt fear of these creatures by many of us and not just the ladies. Although having eight legs they are in the order of Arthropods. They are very numerous and can be found wherever you go ranging in size from 2mm (*Neon reticulatus*) to 20mm in the hunting spiders (*Lycosidae*). They are also quite colourful and nicely marked. We, as a group, had little to no knowledge of their habits and therefore tended to ignore them although we did appreciate their beauty. Some that we saw were very colourful, making them good photographic subjects and as usual I seemed to get the job of identifying it because I had taken its picture!

It was due to one of these pictures that we met Tony White, the County Recorder for spiders. I had photographed a nice green spider, the female of *Micrommata virescens*, which I loaned to the F.C. for one of its displays at the Northampton Show. This was spotted by Tony who commented to the F.C. representative on the stand that it had not been recorded in Northamptonshire and as a result of this we eventually met up. We are now fortunate to have Tony permanently with us and as a result a list of 150 species has been produced for the Estate, some of which are new county records.

Spiders occur in all sorts of habitats, the ones we see easily in our gardens sitting in the middle of a nice big orb web and the dark, fast runners that we disturb in our flower pots in the shed. Nearly every different nook and cranny is selected by different species as their home or lair to where they can retreat for safety or lurk waiting to spring out on some unsuspecting prey. Some like it dry and some like it damp. There is one that lives under water, spinning a web and filling it with air collected from the surface (*Argyroneta aquatica*), not yet recorded on the Estate, and there are others that are directly associated with wet habitats.

The most usual way for spiders to catch their prey is by means of a sticky web, usually orb shaped but there are also other shapes. Some wait in a hole/cavity with trip threads radiating out and ready to dash out and seize whatever has touched them. The jumpers (*Salticidae*) move about very actively waiting for their prey to land near them and then pounce. This type have very good eyesight as the slightest movement near them promotes a reaction. One amusing thing that happens when you examine them with a small, high powered, hand lens is that they will look up at you and then jump upwards in a loop and land on the underside of the lens. Do they possibly see their own reflection? The other jumper/pouncer type are the crab spiders (*Thomisidae*) which do have a crab-like appearance and will wait on the underside of a flower, or maybe on top, for an insect to alight on the flower. They jump out on this insect as it takes nectar, the spider can take something as big as a butterfly and when it jumps it lets out a silk life-line in case it misses the target or is dislodged by the struggles of the prey. Most of these spiders are coloured various shades of brown but there are some that are brightly coloured white or yellow.

Their eggs are all encased in a silken cocoon of various shapes, some being carried about by the female, others attached to firmer substrates. Some will be encased in mud and others looking like little white goblets suspended from a twig or leaf.

All spiders are predatory and carnivorous and kill their prey by injecting venom. Unlike adult insects which do not increase in size once they have reached imago state, spiders do have to moult their exoskeleton in order to allow the soft body to expand. Their web of silk is very strong, as we all know when walking through one in the woods, and is capable of holding quite large prey. The largest I have seen caught was a pair of mating damselflies. I have to admit that the spider did seem a bit surprised when it saw the size of its catch, it took a few seconds before it could make up its mind which one to kill first. The fact that the pair were still coupled helped him. It took it some time to eventually kill and separate them which allowed me plenty of time to photograph the action. Some insects, when caught, are discarded because of the difficulty or danger in tangling with such things as hornets and bees. In such instances the spider will usually cut it free from the web and then set about carrying out repairs to the web.

Quite often webs can be seen but no spider is visible, it is probably waiting either in a hole or behind a leaf. If it is in the vicinity it can be enticed out, without destroying the web, by holding a vibrating tuning fork against one of the lines holding the web. So if you do see someone in the woods waving a tuning fork about he is not trying to compose a new pastoral symphony!

This can only be a brief, general description of the habits of this small but very versatile creature. They really are worth observing more closely and they certainly do their part in keeping down the fly population.

Reptiles and Amphibians

Moving now on to the bigger things takes us into the reptiles and amphibians. The Estate has a very good population of these animals which is certainly helped by the large number of ponds and lakes situated about the area and of course includes the great crested newt, its presence being one of the main reasons for a large part of our woodland being declared a S.S.S.I.

Our reptile population consists of the Grass Snake – *Natrix natrix* and the Slow-worm – *Anguis fragilis*. The grass snake is probably the best known and most often seen. It is very fond of basking on a sunny bank although they usually see you first and glide swiftly away. They are very fond of water habitats and are excellent swimmers and can often be seen swimming across a pond or resting in the weed with just its head above the water surface. It is a skilful hunter in this environment and a large snake will take fish and frogs though the favourite food of young snakes is tadpoles. The female can reach a length of 150cm and will emerge from hibernation in March/April and a short time after will mate. Eggs are laid in the summer. They are soft shelled, about the size of a pigeon's egg, and are laid in decaying plant material as the eggs need warmth and humidity. The newly hatched young measure 15-20cm.

The slow-worm, at first sight, can be confused with a snake but is in fact a legless lizard. We have a good number of these lizards throughout our woods and rides wherever there are logs and stones to hide under. They too like basking in the sun and with care they can be observed for some time. The secret is not to move about too much when they have been spotted, they are much easier to photograph than grass snakes. The female bears live young wrapped in a transparent membrane which ruptures almost immediately producing young lizards 70-100mm long. The birth usually numbers eight young which are coloured black below and golden yellow above with a black line running down the back, quite striking.

We also have a good amphibian population of frogs and toads and all three newts, the main contender here being the Great Crested – *Triturus cristatus*. This is the largest British newt, 13-15cm long, and is black and warty with the male having a large crest running the length of its body and tail. This crest is absent in the female. The belly of both the male and female is bright orange with black markings. This newt is a nationally protected species and it is illegal to handle them without a licence. They are widespread but local mainly in the midlands and south-east England but the species has declined over the past 50 years. They occur on the Estate in large numbers due to the numerous fish-free ponds situated in the woods and they are also in the ornamental ponds in the gardens. From March onwards the female lays about 200 – 400 eggs by attaching them singly to the leaves of water plants. They hatch into tadpoles which have usually developed and left the pond by September although there is a high mortality rate amongst the eggs. It will be three to four years before the young newts become sexually mature and return to the water to breed.

We also have the Smooth or Common newt – *T. vulgaris* which occurs in most of the ponds and backwaters of the lakes although the commercially stocked fish waters are not a favourite place. We have one or two locations for the Palmate newt – *T. helveticus*, this is the smallest of our three newts, not exceeding 75mm, and it prefers slightly more acidic water. It is a very rare newt in the Midlands and is not that common nationally. This newt perhaps needs more attention and research that we now give to the great crested newt. Is it neglected because it is not such a noticeable creature?

Frogs and toads are well scattered over the Estate but have only recently been recorded in the MoD created ponds. Some frog spawn was introduced to a pond in the still active MoD area in 1987 and the hatchings from this have now become well established and are spreading to other ponds in the area.

Frogs are being reported as being drastically in decline and while this is to some extent true due to the filling of old field ponds they are now moving into towns. There are now so many town gardens with ponds that they are adapting to a new environment, either by their own efforts or the introduction of spawn and tadpoles. Toads are just beginning to move into the woodland ponds but there are very few at this point in time. We have not been able to locate a breeding site as yet but one or two young toads have been seen.

Birds

I think we should leave the ground for a while and now take to the air. Birds give us the pleasure of both sight and song when walking through the woods and fields. The song is always best at dawn or dusk but a bright sunny day will encourage them to sing, especially in the mating season. Bird song generally in the day will decline once the excitement of breeding is gone. Nightingales are renowned for their song and quite rightly but there are other equally good soloists well worth listening for. We have recorded 105 species, both breeding and migratory, throughout the Estate, excluding budgerigars, peacocks and parakeets. Unfortunately the numbers are declining when compared with the 80s. Our biggest expanses of water are the park lakes together with Scotland and Grendon Quarter ponds. These waters support a good variety of water associated species, swans, canada geese, various ducks, grebes (gt. crested and little), coot, moorhen, kingfisher and other species. Grey wagtails have been observed nesting in most years and goldeneye have also been seen. In 1997 a pair of egyptian geese flew in and stayed with us and have produced three young which are still with us.

The bunker ponds in the woods have brought in quite a few ducks since being cleared and opened up, mainly mallard and also the occasional teal. There is of course the ever present coot and moorhen although their numbers have severely declined this past 15 years. Since we started to clear the thick scrub in Sane Copse that had grown up around the pond edges we have had other species take up residence. The little grebe (dabchick) and tufted duck were the first newcomers to start breeding and then the canada geese. Most of the nests of the canada geese have been predated by foxes but we have had one or two successful broods. We do get an occasional visit from a mandarin duck and sometimes a pair.

The little grebe does well on the bunker ponds and each year provides us with four to eight nests. It is a very quick little diving bird, diving under at the first signs of disturbance and you have to stand very still to see it re-appear, often some distance from where it went down. Its nest is very different from the accepted version (twigs and grass) being a small heap of wet aquatic vegetation on the edge of a reed bed. When first seen the nest always appears to be empty as the female very rapidly covers the eggs when leaving the nest. If you see a nest (they are nearly always well away from the pond edge) which appears flat or slightly concave on top then it is empty, probably last year's nest. But if there is a slight dome to it, then it will contain eggs.

Wild Tulip – *Tulipa sylvestris*

Abraham–Isacc--Jacob – *Trachystemon orientalis*

Pond clearance (Star pond) using a mini digger

Greater Spearwort – *Ranunculus lingua*

Spring Snowflake – *Leucojum vernum*

Yellow Figwort – *Scrophularia vernalis*

Winter Aconite – *Eranthis hyernalis*

Foxglove Tree – *Paulownia tomentosa*

White Butterbur – *Petasites albus*

Hazel - *Corylus avellana* ♂ ♀

Winter Heliotrope – *Petasites fragrans*

Horse Chestnut, the 'Family Tree', over 200 yrs. old
–*Aesculus hippocastanum*

Bunker pond, reflections

Spindle Fruit – *Euonymus europaeus*

Honeysuckle showing tree damage

Weeping Beech – *Fagus sylvatica-pendula*

Bird's Nest Orchid – *Neottia nidus-avis*

Blue–eyed Mary – *Omphalodes verna*

False Oxlip – *Primula vulgaris x veris*

Common Spotted Orchid – *Dactylorchis fuchsii*

Herb Paris – *Paris quadrifolia*

Narrow–leaved Everlasting Pea - *Lathyrus sylvestris*

Lousewort - *Pedicularis sylvatica*

Woolly Thistle – *Cirsium eriophorum*

Reed Mace, Greater & Lesser – *Typha latifolia T.angustifolia*

Fleabane & Sneezewort – *Pulicaria dysenterica &*
Achillea ptarmica

Adders Tongue fern – *Ophioglossum vulgatum*

Bracket fungus – *Rigidoporus ulmarius*, surporting the
weight of George

Stinkhorn – *Phallus impudicus*

Green Woodcup fungus – *Chlorosplenium aeruginascens*

Morel – *Morchella semilibera*

Ergot fungus – *Claviceps purpurea*

Parrot Wax Cap fungus – *Hygrocybe psittacina*

Brimstone butterfly – *Gonepteryx rhamni*

Black Hairstreak butterfly – *Strymonidia pruni*

Green Hairstreak butterfly – *Callophrys rubi*

Wood White butterfly – *Leptidea sinapis*

White Admiral butterfly – *Ladoga camilla*

Wall butterfly – *Lasiommata megera*

Holly Blue butterfly – Celastrina argiolus ♀

Cinnabar moth larva

Cinnabar moth – *Hypocrita jacobaeae*

Common Blue butterfly – *Polyommatus icarus*

Hornet Clearwing moth, pair – *Sesia apiformis*

Emperor moth – *Saturnia pavonia*, ♀ top, ♂ bottom

Emperor moth larva

Plume moth – *Alucita galactodactyla*

Small Eggar moth – *Eriogaster lanestris*, tent with larvae

Moth leaf mine on beech– *Stigmella tityrella*

Hornet nest (*Vespa crabro*) in high seat

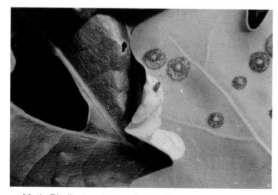

Moth *Phyllonorycter harrisella*. Pupa case on empty mine. Spangle galls on the right

Free hanging wasp nest (*Vespula vulgaris*), probably predated by a woodpecker

Wood Wasp (Horntail) – *Urocerus gigas* ♀

Knopper gall (cynipid wasp) – *Andricus quercuscalisis*

Bramble gall (cynipid wasp) – *Lasioptera rubi*

Oak Apple gall (cynipid wasp) – *Biorhiza pallida*

Fasciation of spear thistle fusing six heads

Green Shield-bug – *Palomena prasina*

Froghopper – *Cercopsis vulnerata*

Southern Hawker dragonfly – *Aeshna cyanea* ♀

Dragonfly (exvuia) – *Libellula quadrimaculata*, showing
white tracheal sacs

Azure Damselfly – *Coenagrion puella* ♂

Spotted Longhorn beetle – *Strangalia maculata*

Longhorn beetle – *Agapanthia villosoviridescens* ♀

Burying beetle – *Nicrophorus vespilloides*

Glow–worm beetle, pair – *Lampyris noctiluca*

Orb type spider web on privet

Spider – *Micrommata viriscens* ♀

Crab spider – *Misumena vatia* ♀

Com. Blue damselflies caught in web of *Larinioides cornutus* ♀

Great Crested newt – *Triturus cristatus* ♀

Great Crested newt – *Triturus cristatus* ♂

Slow-worm - *Anguis fragilis* ♀

Little Grebe nest with eggs

Barn owl – *Tyto alba*

Woodcock nest with eggs

Little Owl pellet, showing beetle elytra

Grey Squirrel – *Sciurus carolinensis*

Fallow deer fawn – *Dama dama*

Muntjac damage to saplings

Muntjac deer – *Muntiacus reevesi* ♂

Red deer, young stag – *Cervus elaphus*

The tufted duck is a smart little chap who started coming to the ponds in the late 80s and we now see up to ten pairs each year most of which hatch off a brood.

Raptors are seen in varying numbers but again appear to be down on the records of the early 80s although we still have our regulars: kestrel, sparrowhawk, with one to three goshawks being seen each year mainly over the Sane Copse and Ravenstone areas. Buzzards are seen flying regularly with an occasional sighting of a hobby, red kite and peregrine.

An unobtrusive and secretive little bird, often heard but not seen, is the grasshopper warbler. It favours low undergrowth such as recently cleared woodland blocks in wet or dry habitats. It is very pleasing to hear the mechanical reeling song, sounding a bit like a fisherman's reel unwinding and can last for a minute or two. They are scattered through the main Chase area and some years up to twelve males have been heard calling.

Crossbills can be seen most years in the conifer blocks. The numbers vary according to the climatic conditions, sometimes just one or two and sometimes a flock of 20 or more. They will work their way along a row of conifers, usually norway spruce, and tear at the cone scales to get at the seed inside. A particularly good year on the Estate was 1997 when small flocks were seen from July and on into May of the following year but no breeding was observed. This sudden large influx was reportedly due to a very poor food year in Scandinavia causing them to migrate earlier than normal.

Owls are always appealing birds and are surrounded by legend and folklore. The tawny owl is often heard calling in the woods, both by day and by night, and one is often disturbed when we push through the understorey, flying off silently not far above our heads.

The little owl quite often gives us a better view of itself as it sits in a tree hole, in a building or on the ground. They do not seem to be so wary of us as other owls. Owl pellets, the undigested remains of their food which they regurgitate, are often found under a favourite roosting place. Little owl pellets can sometimes be found in large numbers under such a roost in a barn where the ground below can be covered with these pellets. They can appear quite shiny when the sun's rays strike them due to the wing cases (elytra) of beetles, these being their favourite food.

Driving along a ride one night, having just finished a mothing session, I spotted a little owl in my headlight beam. I was able to drive right up to it and watch it for a couple of minutes before it decided to retreat back through the grass in search of more beetles.

Long-eared owls have been heard although not every year. We were lucky in 1996 to see them flying and feeding their young. When feeding is taking place there is usually a lot of noise but the young are seldom seen. The most we have seen in any one year is two pairs.

The barn owl was present on a number of Estate locations in the early 80s but reduced greatly in numbers and was completely absent from the early to mid 90s. They started to be seen again in the late 90s and some road casualties started to be found. None of these casualties were ringed which would indicate that they were wild stock. They are now being seen regularly in certain parts of the Estate. Unfortunately, due to their habit of flying very low along roadside hedges and ditches at dusk and dawn, they are very prone to car collisions.

We have one meadow site which has a small stream running through it where one or two snipe can be seen in most years, unfortunately they are only flying through and don't stop to breed.

One bird that can usually be seen flying away from you as you walk through the woods is the woodcock, a mainly solitary bird which has been recorded in all our woodland sections although their numbers do vary from year to year. It is a nocturnal flyer (dusk and dawn) and is usually only seen flying during the day when flushed out of cover when they will run swiftly, unseen, for several metres before take off.

In 1992 George and I had an exciting experience with a woodcock. We were walking quietly through the understorey of Old Pastures wood when we were startled by one which flew straight off the ground immediately in front of us, almost knocking my hat off. Looking down I saw that my feet were straddling a nest containing four eggs, she really had sat tight. My first action was to photograph the eggs and then mark the site. We hoped that she would not desert the nest and on our way back later in the morning saw that she had returned to the nest, not an easy thing to see even when we had marked the site. This was an ideal photographic opportunity but I did not have the right equipment. I contacted a friend who specialised in ornithological photography and a hide was erected the next day, over the next two weeks some very good pictures were taken. My friend achieved shots of the chicks but I only got the empty eggshells. I doubt we will ever see such a picture again.

The female sometimes carries the chicks to the nearest feeding place by holding them between her legs and her body. This action was witnessed once by Colin in 1999.

There have been occasional sightings of the nightjar over the years. They have been seen flying at dusk by patrolling keepers and foresters and once or twice their peculiar churring song has been heard. One positive sighting was made by Colin when carrying out an evening survey in 1998. This bird is not the easiest to spot as it is quite small, about thrush size, its plumage blending in with the background as it rests lengthways along a branch. Unless it is disturbed it only flies at night, catching insects on the wing, and it is only with us from late May to late August so there is not much time to record it.

A pair of green sandpipers were seen for the first time last year (2000) which, although it is a woodland bird, had not previously found the right conditions to encourage it to stay. In a field at the edge of Sane Copse the local farmer had been dumping deep litter refuse from the farm and these large heaps were left there for some time. When they were eventually removed, having reached the right state of maturity, phew, they left behind a scrape which developed into a slurry dip much loved by the local water fowl. It was at this site, then a couple of years old, in August, that the pair were first seen. They stayed for six weeks and were regularly watched by members of the Wild Bunch.

You would indeed be very unlucky if you spent a morning or an afternoon walking through the woods without hearing or seeing a woodpecker. All three of our native woodpeckers are recorded on the Estate, the largest, the green woodpecker, is by far the commonest probably being more heard than seen. Its laughing yaffle carries a long distance and it cannot be mistaken for anything else. It can also be recognised when flying over an open area by its flight pattern, three to four quick wingbeats followed by a long swoop holding its wings along its body.

The great spotted woodpecker is a much smaller bird and announces its presence by drumming on a 'sounding board' such as a broken branch. Both sexes drum with their bills at the rate of 8 – 10 per second for a duration of about one second and the sound carries a long distance.

Our smallest and least common on the Estate is the lesser spotted woodpecker, not much bigger than a sparrow which spends most of its time up in the wood canopy. It also drums on trees and the sound is virtually indistinguishable from the greater. All woodpeckers nest in holes excavated in trees, usually in the older parts of the tree where the wood has started to rot and is softer.

Two little birds that are very scarce on the Estate are the wood warbler and the tree pipit. The wood warbler has occasionally been heard over the past years but it does not appear to have nested and it was not until 1998 that we had a sighting of it. The tree pipit is not a common bird in Northamptonshire and seldom seen on the Estate. It was occasionally seen in the early 90s and then not again until 1998.

Mammals

Coming back down to earth with our mammals, we have recorded 27 species, quite a good number for an ancient woodland site. The larger species are the ones most commonly seen and more easily identified. We can only identify the smaller species, shrews, mice and voles when we find a corpse or are able to dissect an owl pellet. Apart from our colony of pipistrelle bats roosting in the conservation lodge roof and the odd dead body found in an old fallen tree we have to rely on outside observers to provide us with information on bats.

Deer are the most easily spotted because of their size. Our main ones are fallow and muntjac with occasional sightings of roe and chinese water deer. The very occasional red deer, which are escapes from local venison farms, do find their way into the Chase woodlands.

Apart from the red, the roe deer is our only truly native deer on the Estate although it has not yet reached our woodland in any numbers but it could well be breeding here in the next 10 – 15 years.

The fallow is our largest and is maintained in two herds, the Park herd of about 100 strong belonging to the Marquess and those roaming wild in the Chase. This deer is generally accepted as native but it is an introduction from a long time ago. The Romans got some of the blame but most of today's population come from herds brought over by the Normans from Europe. These were the melanistic or black form and were introduced to most of the Royal Forests such as the New, Epping, Dean and locally Salcey. They became a favourite species for sport and park collections and over the centuries fallow now come in a variety of colours, white, menil (brightly spotted which remain so all the year round) and the common, a rich brown with white spots in the summer changing to grey brown without spots in the winter. Due to many escapes from parks and collections, our wild fallow today include all of the above coat colours. The Marquess' private herd contained in the deer park are all melanistic. The wild Chase fallow are predominantly black and common. White ones are occasionally seen and last year (2000) three were seen although these were escapes from the Weston Underwood zoo.

These herds do have to be controlled as today they have no natural predators, bears and wolves, so we have to take over their role. The last British wolf was recorded in the early 1700s. A herd will increase by about 30% per year and our woodland is only capable of supporting a given number of healthy deer.

Regular selective culling has to be carried out annually by the forest rangers to keep the herd number to about 80. This is a skilled operation demanding considerable knoweldge of the deer's habits and lifestyle.

The bucks can cause some tree damage during the rutting season by fraying them with their antlers which are shed annually during the months of April to June. The antlers soon grow again and are stripped of their velvet in August ready for their autumn rut, the fawns being born in June. They are not the easiest animals to photograph unless you have a very long lens or are very lucky, but if you are moving slowly and quietly and the wind is in the right direction you can watch a small group for several minutes. Binoculars are useful here.

They are mainly grass grazers and do browse low herbage, they also have a liking for fallen fruit such as apples and conkers. Generally speaking they cause little serious damage to established woodland although young plantations have to be tubed or fenced off. The tendency these days is to use fences unless the planted area is very small.

Our other common deer is the muntjac. About the size of a fox, the buck has backward curving antlers and also the upper canines are elongated, forming tusks. This deer is another alien introduction from China in the early 1900s when they were kept as tame stock on large estates. Unfortunately many have escaped and have become well established over a large area of southern

England and its range is still expanding. It has no specific mating season, it could be any time and the doe is able to fawn every seven months. Because of their size and habits they are difficult to cull and concentrated efforts have to be regularly made.

They are a serious pest in the woods and forests as they strip bark from saplings and browse all the regenerating growth from coppice stumps. They are most active at night and are very selective in their feeding and will always take the most succulent plants first. If it walks across a grass meadow containing some lush plants, such as orchids, it will always take these first. They are responsible for the loss of many of our orchids on the Estate and it is estimated they are responsible for the loss of about 40% of our bluebells nationally over the past 20 years. They can often be heard barking like a dog, by day and by night. Their distress call is very high pitched and carries a long way. They seem to be rather stupid creatures as when they come across a barrier, such as a cattle fence, they will butt it to try and force their way through and with the 15cm square mesh used today it can get its head trapped. On such an occasion we heard one giving out its panic call, I was with George when we heard it. We tracked it down and found a big buck trapped in the mesh by its antlers. Between us we managed to cut it loose (always carry a pair of pliers in your field bag) when it promptly ran away along the fence and then tried to butt its way through again. They keep to very regular tracks and leave well-worn pathways and tunnels through the low growing vegetation. They are finding their way into village gardens and allotments and into town parks and gardens where they can do a great deal of damage in one night. They may be pleasing to see but again it is costing us money trying to keep another alien species under control and paying for the damage it causes.

One amusing incident with deer that we experienced in 1998 was in the active MoD section. Four of the Wild Bunch had just come out of a wood onto the edge of the south meadow. As always we stopped to scan the meadow for signs of life and on the top of a ditch bank we saw two deer, about 50 metres away. A closer look showed them to be young red deer stags, these escapees are sometimes seen about our woodland. This was the ideal opportunity to try and get a photo of red deer stags so, in my best stalking style and hoping my army camouflage jacket would help conceal me, I crept out into the meadow, keeping a very low profile. Camera cocked, I slowly moved towards them. They began to move, I would like to have been nearer, but it was now or never. I clicked and they moved down into the ditch. Oh well, what could you expect, be satisfied. I stood up and shrugged my shoulders as the other members of the Wild Bunch walked towards me, they were smiling. I looked back at the ditch and saw that the deer had not gone but had come up the opposite bank and were cautiously approaching me. A quick wind on and I was ready for them. I slowly walked towards them looking through the view finder. All was going well, when do I press the button? Hold on chaps, you're getting too close! I had to back away from them to re-compose the picture and I did get some good ones including the Wild Bunch feeding them glucose tablets. When we told the Range Warden about our experience he laughed and explained that the squaddies had taken to feeding them their field rations and that they now associated army camouflage gear with food!

The mole is an animal that is seldom seen and yet evidence of is presence is everywhere we go; runs and mounds and sometimes a fortress, although as yet we have not found one of these on the Estate. Their powerful front legs can move them through the ground at a reasonable speed and if it is just below the surface the raised tunnel can be seen actually moving across the grassland. Sometimes it will poke its snout out into the daylight. Occasionally it will come completely out of the tunnel and run across ground, possibly looking for nesting material, though I have only observed this once. Usually it is only the snout or head that appears followed by a rapid withdrawal back into its run. I was extremely lucky one sunny June day in 1990. I was with Fred and we had been walking for some time. Having run out of puff (Fred that is) we sat down on a grassy bank amongst some mole workings. After a while, sitting very still and quiet, I caught a glimpse of movement out of the corner of my eye. Instinctively raising my camera, always hanging round my neck, I turned my head to see, about two metres away, the ground moving. I hissed at Fred, "Don't move". I watched a little mound of earth erupt, followed by a pink snout. By then my camera was zeroed in. Through the viewfinder I watched a small black head appear and two pink paws. It was sniffing the air, would it come any further? I couldn't wait any longer, I had to push the button. Click, and it rapidly disappeared back into its burrow. "Did you get it?" said Fred. I did!

It is a strong swimmer although it rarely ventures into water, it is useful though if it has set up its tunnel system in an area that is prone to flooding. Its main food consists of earthworms and slugs and periods of very dry weather cause him to have to go much deeper to find his food, under these conditions food can become scarce and it is then that you start to find dead bodies laying around on the surface. These bodies are usually quickly buried by the various carrion beetles. At one time villages had their local mole catcher as they were considered a pest in the vegetable garden and the mole skins were sought after to make waistcoats, often worn by Victorian gamekeepers.

The grey squirrel is very common in the woods and can be seen at all times when walking through them. It often extends out into neighbouring gardens and allotments and is just at home in towns as in the countryside. It was introduced from the Americas in 1876. They were brought over with the deliberate intention of releasing them into English estates and surrounding areas. The releases had some considerable success and they were still being released by misguided people up to the 1920s. They have now become a serious pest to foresters and horticulturalists alike and concentrated efforts have to be made to drastically reduce their numbers. Around the Estate it is referred to as the tree rat.

Although it is considered by some as an appealing little animal, which can become very tame in public parks it does cause a great amount of damage. It can kill young trees by bark stripping, it will take eggs and fledglings of small birds and is quite happy to help itself to your fruit and vegetables. Some years the population can be great enough to cause failure of hazel and beech-mast crops. However appealing you may find him he is costing a lot of money each year paying for the controls that have to be carried out.

The fox is our largest carnivore (by a tail). It is typically a woodland animal although very adaptable in colonising farmland and uplands and is increasingly entering suburbia. It is most active at dusk and night time but it can sometimes be seen by day and I have been lucky enough to have had some very good views of families playing. Its diet is very varied ranging from rodents and birds to beetles and frogs. It is also partial to fruit. In towns it will scavenge refuse, in times of plenty it will cache any surplus. It can be a very destructive animal especially if it finds an insecure henhouse and gamekeepers are continually waging war on them. I have a large pond in my garden, just for wildlife, which has a very large frog population and about two years ago the local fox decided to have a go at my frogs leaving about eight or nine dead bodies for me to find in the morning. In such an event it is necessary to place creosote soaked rags around the pond, this will keep the fox away but make sure that the rags cannot drip into the pond water. It has a very short staccato bark and the vixen is very high pitched, almost a scream, very eerie when heard for the first time at night. The dog has a very distinctive musty odour which lingers on vegetation where the animal has recently passed. It is this odour which always tells us that he is about.

The badger is equally well known but is a much more secretive animal and is mainly nocturnal, it is widely distributed in Britain. On the Estate we have many setts and they have increased in number over the past seven to eight years. These setts are excavated in the ground usually in banks or sloping ground. They prefer light and easy to dig soils and the sett can be quite extensive with several entrances, the sleeping chambers are lined with grass and straw which is frequently brought out for an airing and is regularly replaced.

It tends to amble along well worn tracks at night eating worms, slugs, beetles, amphibians and small mammals, it is also very fond of fruit. Its signs and tracks can often be found, it has its regular play areas and has separate toilets often away from the sett. If it crosses muddy ground it will leave unmistakable paw prints, very broad with five toes and distinctive claw marks. Its strong claws are very useful for breaking into old tree stumps to dig out wasps or bees nests and beetle larva.

Stoats and weasels are frequently seen dashing across the tracks, the stoat being seen more often. One very good sighting that I had of a stoat family on the move was when I had been standing for some time at a gate. I saw a movement along the track which was a stoat running up the track towards me followed by another. The first one was carrying something in its mouth which, as it ran right past my feet, I saw was a stoat kitten and not far behind was mum or perhaps dad carrying another kitten. Moving house? Once passed me they dashed into a ditch and I saw them no more.

We do see the ermine form in the winter. Most years produce sightings of one or two, some just glimpses but on other occasions we have good clear views as they run down a track. Ermine is where its coat turns white except for the black tip to the tail, this winter colour change is more frequent the further north you go.

Mink are beginning to spread onto the Estate. These are vicious predators living mainly on fish but they are also killing off numbers of our common water and ground nesting birds. Whilst they have not, as yet, been seen in any great numbers in our woodlands, they are now being seen more frequently and our many areas of water will make them a good habitat in which to become established. Our larger expanses of water which are stocked with fish will be the main attraction. Our woodland ponds, containing no fish, will not be so attractive.

This animal was brought into the country in the 1920s for fur breeding on commercial farms. In the 1930s badly managed farms allowed animals to escape and even more idiotic are the deliberate releases which have been made since and this has enabled strong feral colonies to develop which are now established over most of Britain.

Hares are seen every year but the populations fluctuate greatly from year to year. They are comical animals with their springtime antics, sparring and boxing. Providing you do not startle them you are usually able to watch them for some time and can, if lucky, get quite close to them. When George and I were walking quietly along a track in 1996 we spotted a large hare ahead grooming itself and immediately stood still so that we could watch it. We were very surprised to see it start loping up the track towards us, we had never stood so motionless, it gradually came right up to us and sniffed my wellies. It decided that was enough and ran off back down the track – who could blame it! This does show however that if you move about the woods slowly and quietly you can be treated to some memorable sights even though it is most unlikely that you will get them on camera.

This seems to have exhausted our tales about the more interesting flora and fauna species that we have studied and recorded as we have walked the Estate over the past years. As mentioned earlier we are a mixed bunch, a bit older now but still sharing the same interest, the countryside, and the past 20 years have given us much pleasure and excitement. Quite a jolly bunch and usually able to see the funny side of things, we have enjoyed a lot of laughs when going about our studies. Some amusing incidents have already been mentioned and many more will be stored in our memories for future reference but one other does spring to mind.

Colin and I were walking the parkland by the lakes when we came across an electrified sheep fence. These are often about the Estate but you never know whether they are switched on or not.

My usual method of crossing these fences is to gently push down the top strand with my walking stick and step over. Now I have long legs, Colin doesn't. Having successfully negotiated the barrier I waited for Colin who doesn't carry a stick. So, he rested his field bag on the top strand to depress it, successfully. However, in his movement to step over, the bag slipped off, causing the top strand to spring upwards between his legs.

The startled look on Colin's face was and still is indescribable, I would like to have helped him but I was staggering about laughing helplessly. Luckily the fence was not switched on so no damage was done and even Colin saw the funny side of it when he found that he could still walk!

Other Sites

Most of that which has been mentioned has centred around the Chase and other woods but there are other interesting areas to be explored. The Engine Pond with its waterwheel (no longer in existence) was used in 1696 to pump water to the Castle. Due to increased demand the system was updated in 1865 and a water tower was built. There is always a good selection of water birds present and it is bounded on the east side by a beautiful glade of winter aconite which flower in the spring. This pond joins, by a small stream, with Paradise Ponds situated at Chadstone. These ponds consist of what appears to be a square moat and mound at the south end, probably of medieval origin. The elaborate arrangement of the connecting ponds were probably constructed in the 18th-19th century for use as fish ponds. These ponds and the surrounding area have provided us with some good botanical records.

The sandpit (now disused) situated adjacent to Cold Oak Copse is a unique habitat in a heavy clay area and has provided us with both botanical and entomological species associated with sand. It is bounded on the north by pasture and a stream flowing east which continues on past an old pumphouse. This stream flows through an old dam some 200 metres long, 25 metres wide and 4 metres high which is now broken in the middle to allow the stream to pass through. When this was a solid dam it would have created a fairly large pond behind it. The date and purpose of this structure is not known although it is most likely to be of medieval origin and there is a clue to its presence on a map of 1760. To the east of the dam there is a slightly raised embankment which was the site of the clubhouse built by the 6th Marquess in the late 1940s to serve the now derelict adjacent golf course. The surrounding meadowland is old ridge and furrow as are many other parts of the Estate meadowland.

There are three ancient veterans often mentioned in the history of the Estate, Gog and Magog oaks and Cowpers oak. Of the first two only Gog is left standing as a sturdy skeleton and is often a host to owls. Magog was unfortunately destroyed by fire some years ago. Cowpers oak, also destroyed by fire in the 1960s, was reputedly an inspiration to the 18th century poet Cowper, who in the late 1700s would walk the three miles from his home in Olney to sit under its spreading branches. It was when he was sheltering under this tree in a heavy thunderstorm that he was inspired to write his hymn 'God moves in a Mysterious Way'.

Reminiscences

I hope you have enjoyed the past twenty years with us and that it will encourage you to get out and enjoy the countryside as much as you can. I think we have been very fortunate in being able to enjoy the colours, sounds and happenings that are around in this patch of undisturbed fields and woodland. This is something which these days, unfortunately, is getting less available to us.

Although I have written about and experienced the pleasure of such countryside it does cause me to look back and reminisce on my younger days. Although being born a 'townie' I have always loved the country and wild living things. In my very young days my nearest countryside was Mitcham Common and Streatham Common, both places I could walk or cycle to. Ponds and trees were plentiful in both of these places and you could always guarantee to find newts and plenty of frog spawn and you didn't need a licence to handle them. There was always the annual pilgrimage with your mates to bring back spawn and rear it through in an old stone sink.

Whenever you sat down in the long grass you always disturbed grasshoppers and could hear them chirping all around you. Any buildings in the area that had overhanging eaves would have house martin nests attached to the walls. Quite often, as a family, we would get on a bus to Shirley Hills for a picnic and watch the red squirrels that were there.

My parents moved to the country, just before the war, to Southwater in Sussex and they took me with them including my cages and boxes of various livestock. This was when I really got the taste for country life. Our cottage, formerly belonging to a gamekeeper, was in the middle of a large, very neglected, wood which had only been used for game. It was very wild. There were no deer about but there were plenty of foxes, in those days they were found mainly in woods, and I regularly watched the occupants of a badger's sett. I would walk all day and in the summer every patch of thistles had dozens of butterflies feeding on them as well as plenty of cinnabar moths. The fields around contained plenty of ragwort. There was one part of the wood which was mainly oak and here you could see purple emperor butterflies, several flying high in the canopy, and sometimes they would come down to bits of carrion that I left about. That was the only time I have ever seen them naturally in any numbers. In June and July the track to our cottage was lined with glow-worms and at night dozens of different moths would flutter at the windows when we lit up the Tilley lamp.

Wild flowers grew in much more profusion and you could still find corn marigold and occasionally some cornflowers on the wide margins of the cornfields. In those days the farmers always left a good wide headland; no cutting through hedge roots in those days. Harvest mouse nests could often be found in tussocks of grass in the vicinity of the cornfield. The tawny owl was always heard at night and barn owls were quite frequent around all the old farm buildings that were in the area and there were plenty of mice and voles to feed them.

The war drastically changed these woods. The fields were taken over by the Ministry of Agriculture and ploughed up and the mature trees were harvested. I'm sure that this may have increased the value of the estate but the woods were never the same again.

You could walk to local pastures, before breakfast, and gather mushrooms every day during their season. Hazelnuts were a crop worth gathering too. The wild fruits in those days were much more harvested than they are today, crab apples, blackberries, sloes and wild strawberries among those favoured. The strawberries cropped extremely well on our south facing fields and made excellent jam, a very different flavour from the cultivated berries. Crab apple jelly was also a great favourite at tea time. During the war period these wild foods did much to supplement our meagre, but healthy, rations. A rabbit, of which there were plenty, in the pot with blackberry and apple pie to follow did much to raise the spirits during those hard times. During the war years rabbits had a good bartering value to 'townies' who would give up their sugar for such things. You could also get a couple of bob for them too.

As the war years went on, mine and other peoples' lives changed drastically. I went back to being a 'townie' again. My love of the country never changed but it did have to become a weekend activity and myxomatosis put paid to any rabbit pie.

It was becoming increasingly obvious that nature's creatures were declining. After the war, lots of new innovations and chemicals were introduced to the land. Not all of these ideas were properly thought through or sufficiently researched, DDT being the villain of the piece. Trends and policies continued to frequently change which made it very difficult for wildlife to cope. Although a lot of protesting was done it was usually a case of shutting the stable door after the horse had bolted.

In spite of all this the countryside has continued to give us all much pleasure and interest. The one topic we are now continually discussing amongst us is the drastically reducing number of insects and birds. The species are still with us but their numbers are just not about any more. As a lad I can remember walking down leafy lanes and you could actually hear the hum of insects about you. Give a bush a whack with a stick and you were instantly surrounded by swarms of flying things and oaks were most prolific in these instances. If you do that today you are lucky to get more than a dozen insects and a couple of spiders. Only about two years ago George and I beat the lower branches of a dozen oaks which produced between them six caterpillars, several ladybirds and a couple of lacewings and a few miscellaneous flies and spiders. In the years gone by it would have taken us all of that time to sort out the catch from just two or three trees.

Buddleia bushes, michelmas daisies and such like always had plenty of butterflies feeding on the nectar and whenever you did some gardening you would always disturb a garden tiger moth, angleshades or magpie moth, but no more. If you ran a moth trap at night you could get hundreds coming in, now they come in tens and twenties. It is always headline news for a few days when a species is threatened and quite rightly, but who is counting the numbers. It is not just insects but bird numbers which are also well down, as are some plants.

Yes, it's good to reminisce and sad to say that those days will not come back. It is doubtful even if we will be able to hold our own. I can't help feeling that if someone else comes along in fifty years time to survey the Estate again and they see our records, which I hope they will do, the comment made will, I'm sure, be "they never saw that here!"

Index of Sections: O/S Landranger series No.152

Yardley Chase, sections 1 – 6
Eastern Block, sections 7 – 9

Garden, Sandpit, Quarry etc., sections 10 onwards.

Section
1. SP876549.	Old Pond Close, including hedge and pond to the west connecting with section 5.
2. SP850530.	Ravenstone Road Copse (Barnstable Wood) including Roadleys Brake and Hangers Spinney to the south, and to the east Dinglederry and Ash Beds. Part SSSI.
3. SP840550.	MoD (Buntingsea and Northampton Copse, Colliers Hern). All SSSI.
4. SP855540.	Sane Copse (ex MoD), all SSSI.
5. SP865543.	Olney Lane End, Grimpsey Copse, Howbrooke Copse and Church Slade, incorporating Biggin Lodge area.
6. SP847565.	Denton Wood, Whiston Pike Copse, Young Ausway, Little Hay Copse, Chase Park and avenue area.
7. SP885563.	Long Furlong and Old Pastures with Hills Copse and Spotley corner, including hedges running north to Cold Oak Copse (S9).
8. SP897575.	Horn Wood.
9. SP880575.	Cold Oak Copse and Easton Hickel.
10 SP865590.	Castle Ashby gardens and surrounding area bounded by the road to the north, and west to Whiston road (sewage farm).
11 SP874580.	Sand pit and meadow situated north-west of Cold Oak Copse (S9).
12 SP840603.	Old quarry and surrounding area (The Firs and Whiston Spinney) extending east to cover the pond and stream to Whiston road.

Flora

Taxon	Vernacular	Recorded sections
Abies grandis	Grand Fir	5
Acer campestre	Field Maple	1-12
Acer pseudoplatanus	Sycamore	1-11
Achillea millefolium	Yarrow	1-6 8-11
Achillea ptarmica	Sneezewort	3-6
Aconitum napellus	Monkshood	10
Aegopodium podagraria	Ground Elder	6
Aesculus carnea	Red Horse Chestnut	3 6
Aesculus hippocastanum	Horse Chestnut	1-11
Aethusa cynapium	Fool's Parsley	2 5 7 9
Agrimonia eupatoria	Agrimony	1-7 9 10 12
Ajuga reptans	Bugle	1-12
Alcea rosea	Hollyhock	2
Alchemilla filicaulis ssp. vestita	Common Lady's mantle	1 6 11
Alisma lanceolatum	Narrow-leaved Water-plantain	square V3
Alisma plantago-aquatica	Water-plantain	1-4 6 10
Alliaria petiolata	Garlic Mustard	1 2 6
Allium ursinum	Ramsons	1 4
Alnus glutinosa	Alder	1-7 10 12
Alnus incana	Grey Alder	4
Anagallis arvensis	Scarlet Pimpernel	1-8 10 11
Anemone apennina	Blue Anemone	10
Anemone nemorosa	Wood Anemone	2-4 7-10
Angelica sylvestris	Wild Angelica	1-12
Anthemis cotula	Stinking Chamomile	1-3 5 7
Anthriscus sylvestris	Cow Parsley	1-12
Aphanes arvensis agg.	Parsley Piert	12
Apium nodiflorum	Fool's Water-cress	1-4 11
Aquilegia vulgaris	Columbine	2 10
Arabidopsis thaliana	Thale Cress	1 6
Arctium minus	Lesser Burdock	1-12
Arenaria serpyllifolia .	Thyme-leaved Sandwort	3 4
Arenaria serpyllifolia ssp. leptoclados	Slender Sandwort	34
Armoracia rusticana	Horse-radish	11
Artemisia absinthium	Wormwood	2
Artemisia vulgaris	Mugwort	1 2 5 6 8 10 11
Arum maculatum	Lords and Ladies	1-12
Asplenium adiantum-nigrum	Black Spleenwort	2 10
Asplenium ruta-muraria	Wall Rue	2 10
Asplenium trichomanes	Maidenhair Spleenwort	2
Astragalus glycyphyllos	Wild Liquorice	2 11
Athyrium filix-femina	Lady Fern	2-4 6-8
Atriplex patula	Common Orache	7 11
Atriplex prostrata	Halberd-leaved Orache	11
Atropa belladonna	Deadly Nightshade	10
Ballota nigra	Black Horehound	2 5 9 11
Barbarea vulgaris	Common Winter Cress	1-8 10 11
Bellis perennis	Daisy	1-12
Betula pendula	Silver Birch	1-10 12
Betula pubescens	Downy Birch	1-3 7 8
Blackstonia perfoliata	Yellow-wort	2
Bryonia dioica	White Bryony	1-11
Buxus sempervirens	Box	2 3 10
Callitriche platycarpa	Various-leaved Water-starwort	2-5 10 11
Callitriche stagnalis sens. lat.	Common Water-starwort	1 6-8 10
Caltha palustris	Marsh Marigold	2 10 12

Calystegia sepium	Hedge / Great Bindweed	1 2 4 6 7 10 11
Campanula latifolia	Giant Bellflower	2
Campanula rotundifolia	Harebell	3
Campanula trachelium	Nettle-leaved Bellflower	1 2 4 6-10
Capsella bursa-pastoris	Shepherd's Purse	2 3 7 9-12
Cardamine flexuosa	Wavy Bitter-cress	6
Cardamine hirsuta	Hairy Bitter-cress	1 3 4 8 11
Cardamine pratensis	Lady's Smock	1-10 12
Carduus crispus	Welted Thistle	1 3 4 6 8-11
Carduus nutans	Musk Thistle	2 10 11
Carpinus betulus	Hornbeam	1-5 7
Cedrus atlantica	Atlas Cedar	square K4, Q1
Cedrus libani	Cedar of Lebanon	10
Centaurea nigra	Comm. Knapweed / Hardhead	1-12
Centaurea scabiosa	Greater Knapweed	2 3 11
Centaurium erythraea	Common Centaury	2--9
Cerastium fontanum	Common Mouse-ear	1-12
Cerastim glomeratum	Sticky Mouse-ear	2-4
Chaenorhinum minus	Small Toadflax	2-4
Chaerophyllum temulum	Rough Chervil	1 7 8
Chamerion angustifolium	Rosebay Willowherb	1-12
Chelidonium majus	Greater Celandine	10
Chenopodium album	Fat Hen	1-4 10-12
Chenopodium polyspermum	Many-seeded Goosefoot	3 6
Chenopodium rubrum	Red Goosefoot	2 4 10 11
Circaea lutetiana	Enchanter's Nightshade	1-9 12
Cirsium acaule	Dwarf Thistle	2 3 11
Cirsium acaule v. caulescens	Dwarf Thistle	3
Cirsium arvense	Creeping Thistle	1-12
Cirsium eriophorum	Woolly Thistle	2-4 12
Cirsium palustre	Marsh Thistle	1-11
Cirsium vulgare	Spear Thistle	1-12
Clematis vitalba	Traveller's Joy	1-7 9 10
Clinopodium vulgare	Wild Basil	1 2 7-9 11
Conium maculatum	Hemlock	2 4 5 11
Conopodium majus	Pignut	2-11
Consolida ajacis	Larkspur	2
Convolvulus arvensis	Field Bindweed	1-3 5 7 8 10 11
Conyza canadensis	Canadian Fleabane	8 11
Cornus sanguinea	Dogwood	1-11
Coronopus squamatus	Swinecress	2 3 11
Corydalis cava	Hollow-root	10
Corydalis solida	Bird-in-a-bush	10
Corylus avellana	Hazel	1-11
Crataegus laevigata	Midland Hawthorn	1-4 6-12
Crataegus monogyna	Hawthorn	1-12
Crepis biennis	Rough Hawksbeard	2
Crepis capillaris	Smooth Hawksbeard	2 3 10 11
Crepis vesicaria	Beaked Hawksbeard	2
Cymbalaria muralis	Ivy-leaved Toadflax	2 10. 11
Cytisus scoparius	Broom	2
Dactylorhiza fuchsii	Common Spotted Orchid	1-10 12
Dactylorhiza maculata	Heath Spotted Orchid	3
Daphne laureola	Spurge Laurel	1 2 6 7 9 10
Daucus carota ssp. carota	Wild Carrot	2-7 10
Digitalis purpurea	Foxglove	1 2 4 7 11
Dipsacus fullonum sens. lat.	Wild Teasel	1-12
Doronicum pardalianches	Leopard's-bane	10
Dryopteris affinis ssp. borreri	Scaly Male Fern	3 6
Dryopteris carthusianaa	Narrow Buckler-Fern	1-6 8

Dryopteris dilatata	Broad Buckler Fern	1-6
Dryopters filix-mas agg.	Common Male Fern	1-10 12
Echium vulgare	Viper's Bugloss	2
Elodea canadensis	Canadian Pondweed	2
Epilobium ciliatum	American Willowherb	1 2 5-9
Epilobium hirsutum	Great Willowherb	1-12
Epilobium montanum	Broad-leaved Willowherb	1-11
Epilobium parviflorum	Hoary Willowherb	2-8
Epipactis helleborine	Broad-leaved Helleborine	1-4 6 7 9
Epipactis purpurata	Violet Helleborine	4 5 7
Equisetum arvense	Field Horsetail	1-7 10-12
Equisetum fluviatile	Water Horsetail	3
Equisetum palustre	Marsh Horsetail	1-6
Equisetum telmateia	Giant Horsetail	4 12
Eranthis hyemalis	Winter Aconite	6 10
Erigeron acer	Blue Fleabane	4 11
Erodium cicutarium	Common Stork's-bill	2-4
Erophila verna sens. lat.	Common Whitlow Grass	3 4
Euonymus europaeus	Spindle	1-5 7-10
Eupatorium cannabinum	Hemp-agrimony	1-10
Euphorbia amygdaloides	Wood Spurge	4
Euphorbia exigua	Dwarf Spurge	1 2 5-7 11
Euphorbia helioscopia	Sun Spurge	11
Euphorbia peplus	Petty Spurge	2 3 7
Euphrasia officinalis agg.	Eyebright	1-7
Fagus sylvatica	Beech	1-7 9 10
Fallopia convolvulus	Black Bindweed	2-4 6 8 10-12
Fallopia japonica	Japanese Knotweed	2
Filago vulgaris	Common Cudweed	square V3
Filipendula ulmaria	Meadowsweet	1-12
Filipendula vulgaris	Dropwort	3 7
Fragaria vesca	Wild Strawberry	1-10
Fraxinus excelsior	Ash	1-12
Fumaria officinalis	Common Fumitory	2 11
Galanthus nivalis	Snowdrop	2 10
Galeopsis tetrahit agg.	Common Hemp-nettle	2 5
Galium aparine	Cleavers / Goosegrass	1-12
Galium mollugo	Hedge Bedstraw	1-11
Galium odoratum	Woodruff	5
Galium palustre	Marsh Bedstraw	1-8
Galium verum	Lady's Bedstraw	1-4 6-8 11 12
Galium mollugo x verum	Lady's Bedstraw (hybrid)	2
Geranium dissectum	Cut-leaved Crane's-bill	1-4 6-12
Geranium lucidum	Shining Crane's-bill	6
Geranium molle	Dove's-foot Crane's-bill	1 3 5 10 11
Geranium pratense	Meadow Crane's-bill	1-4 6 10
Geranium pusillum	Small-flowered Crane's-bill	2 8
Geranium pyrenaicum	Hedgerow Crane's-bill	1 10 11
Geranium robertianum	Herb Robert	1-12
Geum rivale	Water Avens	2 10
Geum urbanum	Wood Avens	1-11
Glechoma hederacea	Ground Ivy	1-12
Gnaphalium uliginosum	Marsh Cudweed	2-7 9
Hedera helix	Ivy	1-12
Helleborus foetidus	Stinking Hellebore	3 10
Helleborus viridis	Green Hellebore	10
Heracleum mantegazzianum	Giant Hogweed	10

Heracleum sphondylium	Hogweed	1-12
Hesperis matronalis	Dame's Violet	3 4 7 11
Humulus lupulus	Hop	4 11 12
Hyacinthoides non-scripta	Bluebell	1-12
Hyacinthoides non-scripta v. bracteosa	Bracted Bluebell	8 10
Hypericum hirsutum	Hairy St. John's-wort	1-10 12
Hypericum maculatum	Imperforate St. John's-wort	7
Hypericum perforatum	Perforate St. John's-wort	2-10
Hypericum tetrapterum	Square-stalked St. John's-wort	1 2 4 6-9
Hypochaeris radicata	Common Catsear	3
Ilex aquifolium	Holly	2-5 8 10 12
Inula conyzae	Ploughman's-spikenard	square P4
Iris foetidissima	Stinking Iris	5 10
Iris pseudacorus	Yellow Flag	2 4 10-12
Juglans regia	Walnut	10
Kickxia elatine	Sharp-leaved Fluellen	2-9
Kickxia spuria	Round-leaved Fluellen	2 3 6-9
Knautia arvensis	Field Scabious	2 5 6 11 12
Laburnum anagyroides	Laburnum	10 11
Lactuca serriola	Prickly Lettuce	2 3 7 8 10-12
Lamiastrum galeobdolon	Yellow Archangel	1-3 6 8
Lamium album	White Dead Nettle	1-12
Lamium amplexicaule	Henbit Dead Nettle	1 3 8
Lamium hybridum	Cut-leaved Dead Nettle	12
Lamium purpureum	Red Dead Nettle	1 2 6-8 10-12
Lapsana communis	Nipplewort	1-12
Larix decidua	Larch	1-3 6 7 10-12
Lathyrus latifolius	Broad-leaved Everlasting-pea	2
Lathyrus pratensis	Meadow Vetchling	1 2 4-7 9
Lathyrus sylvestris	Narrow-leaved Everlasting-pea	3 8 9
Legousia hybrida	Venus's Looking Glass	2
Lemna minor	Common Duckweed	2-6 8-11
Lemna trisulca	Ivy-leaved Duckweed	3 4
Leontodon autumnalis	Autumnal Hawkbit	6
Leontodon hispidus	Rough Hawkbit	1-12
Leontodon saxatilis	Lesser Hawkbit	3
Lepidium campestre	Field Pepperwort	2 11
Leucanthemum vulgare	Oxeye Daisy	2-7 10 11
Leucojum vernum	Spring Snowflake	10
Ligustrum vulgare	Wild Privet	1-11
Linaria purpurea	Purple Toadflax	4 10 11
Linaria vulgaris	Common Toadflax	2 3 6 10
Linum catharticum	Fairy Flax	2 5 6 8
Linum usitatissimum	Cultivated Flax	5
Listera ovata	Common Twayblade	1-4 8
Lithospermum officinale	Common Gromwell	1 2 4-6
Lonicera periclymenum	Honeysuckle	1-11
Lotus corniculatus	Common Bird's-foot Trefoil	2-8 10
Lotus pedunculatus	Large Bird's-foot Trefoil	1-9
Lunaria annua	Honesty	2 10
Lychnis flos-cuculi	Ragged Robin	1-10
Lycopus europaeus	Gipsywort	2-5 8
Lysimachia nummularia	Creeping Jenny	1-10 12
Lysimachia vulgaris	Yellow Loosestrife	2 4
Lythrum salicaria	Purple Loosestrife	2 4 7 10
Malus sylvatica	Crab Apple	1-11

Malva moschata	Musk-mallow	2 4 10
Malva neglecta	Dwarf Mallow	2
Malva sylvestris	Common Mallow	2 10-12
Matricaria discoidea	Pineapple Weed	1 4 5 7-12
Matricaria recutita	Scented Mayweed	1 2 7 9
Medicago lupulina	Black Medick	23 6-9
Medicago sativa ssp. sativa	Lucerne	2
Melilotus altissimus	Tall Melilot	2
Melilotus officinalis	Ribbed Melliot	2
Mentha aquatica	Water Mint	2-8 10-12
Mentha arvensis	Corn Mint	1 2 4-10 12
Mentha x verticillata	Whorled Mint	7 9
Menyanthes trifoliata	Bogbean (introduced)	2
Mercurialis perennis	Dog's Mercury	1-10
Moehringia trinervia	Three-nerved Sandwort	1-3 6-9
Myosotis arvensis	Field Forget-me-not	1-12
Myosotis discolor	Changing Forget-me-not	3 4
Myosotis laxa	Tufted Forget-me-not	3
Myosotis scorpioides	Water Forget-me-not	3
Myosoton aquaticum	Water Chickweed	8
Neottia nidus-avis	Bird's-nest Orchid	7
Nicandra physalodes	Apple-of-Peru	2
Nuphar lutea	Yellow Water-lily	10
Nymphaea alba	White Water-lily	3 10
Odontites vernus	Red Bartsia	2-7 9-12
Omphalodes verna	Blue-eyed Mary	square P4 only
Ononis repens	Rest-harrow	11
Ononis spinosa	Spiny Rest-harrow	2 3
Onopordum acanthium	Scotch Thistle	2
Ophioglossum vulgatum.	Adder's Tongue	1 3-6
Ophrys apifera	Bee Orchid	2-4 10
Orchis mascula	Early Purple Orchid	1-7 9 10
Origanum vulgare	Wild Marjoram	9 11
Oxalis acetosella	Wood Sorrel	1-8 10
Papaver dubium ssp. dubium	Long-headed Poppy	2-4 11 12
Papaver dubium ssp. lecoqii	Yellow-juiced Poppy	4
Papaver rhoeas	Corn Poppy	1-4 7 8 10 11
Papaver somniferum	Opium Poppy	2 11
Parietaria judaica	Pellitory-of-the-Wall	10
Paris quadrifolia	Herb Paris	1-7
Pastinaca sativa	Wild Parsnip	8
Pedicularis sylvatica	Lousewort	3
Pentaglottis sempervirens	Green Alkanet	11
Persicaria amphibia	Amphibious Bistort	2 10 11
Persicaria bistorta	Bistort	2 10 11
Persicaria hydropiper	Water-pepper	6 7 9
Persicaria lapathifolia	Pale Persicaria	3 4 7
Persicaria maculosa	Redshank	2-11
Petasites albus	White Butterbur	10
Petasites fragrans	Winter Heliotrope	10
Petasites hybridus	Butterbur	10
Phyllitis scolopendrium	Harts Tongue Fern	2-4 12
Picea abies	Norway Spruce	2 3 5-8 10 12
Picea sitchensis	Sitka Spruce	7
Picris echioides	Bristly Oxtongue	1 2 4-11
Pilosella aurantiaca	Fox and Cubs	3 4
Pilosella officinarum	Mouse-ear Hawkweed	2
Pimpinella major	Greater Burnet Saxifrage	1 2 5-9 11

Pimpinella saxifraga	Burnet Saxifrage	3 11
Pinus sylvestris	Scots Pine	1-3 5-7 10 12
Plantago lanceolaata	Ribwort Plantain	1-12
Plantago major	Greater Plantain	1-12
Plantago media	Hoary Plantain	2 5 10 11
Platanthera chlorantha	Greater Butterfly Orchid	1-3 7
Polygala vulgaris	Common Milkwort	3 4
Polygonum aviculare	Knot-grass	2 3 6-8 11
Populus alba	White poplar	12
Populus canescens	Grey poplar	36 12
Populus x canadensis	Black Italian poplar	168
Populus x gileadensis	Balsam poplar	6
Potamogeton alpinus	Pondweed reddish	3
Potamogeten berchtoldii	Pondweed slender	34
Potamogeten crispus	Pondweed curly	34
Potamogeten lucens	Pondweed shining	34
Prunus insititia	Bullace	P3
Pseudotsuga menziesii	Douglas fir	35
Quercus ilex	Holme Oak	10
Quercus petraea	Sessile Oak	1-5 9-11
Quercus pyrenaica	Pyrenean Oak	5
Quercus robur	Pedunculate Oak	1-12
Quercus rubra	Red Oak	1 3 7
Quercus seris	Turkey Oak	1-7 10 12
Ranunculus acris	Meadow Buttercup	1-7 10 12
Ranunculus aquatilis	Common Water Crowfoot	1 4-6 10 11
Ranunculus auricomus	Goldilocks Buttercup	2-4 7 9 10
Ranunculus bulbosus	Bulbous Buttercup	2-5 7-10
Ranunculus ficaria	Lesser Celandine	1-12
Ranunculus flammula	Lesser Spearwort	1 3 4
Ranunculus lingua	Greater Spearwort	10
Ranunculus peltatus	Pond Water Crowfoot	square V3 only
Ranunculus repens	Creeping Buttercup	1-12
Ranunculus sceleratus	Celery-leaved Buttercup	4
Ranunculus trichophyllus	Thread-leaved Water Crowfoot	2 6
Raphanus raphanistrum	Wild Radish	5
Reseda alba	White Mignonette	2
Reseda lutea	Wild Mignonette	2
Reseda luteola	Weld	2 4 11
Rhamnus cathartica	Buckthorn	1 2 4 7 11
Rhinanthus minor	Yellow Rattle	1 2 5 7 9
Rhus hirta	Sumac	11
Ribes nigrum	Black Currant	6 9
Ribes rubrum	Red Currant	1-7 9
Ribes uva-crispa	Gooseberry	5
Robinia pseudoacacia	False Acacia	3
Rorippa nasturtium-aquaticum	Water Cress	1-3 6 7 10 11
Rosa arvensis	Field Rose	1-12
Rosa canina agg.	Dog Rose	1-12
Rosa pimpinellifolia	Burnet Rose	2
Rosa rubiginosa agg.	Sweet Briar	5
Rubus caesius	Dewberry	1-10
Rubus fruticosus agg.	Bramble	1-12
Rubus idaeus	Raspberry	7
Rumex acetosa	Common Sorrel	1-12
Rumex acetosella	Sheep's Sorrel	9
Rumex conglomeratus	Clustered Dock	2 3
Rumex crispus	Curled Dock	1-4 6 8-11
Rumex obtusifolius	Broad-leaved Dock	1-12

Rumex sanguineus	Wood Dock	1-11
Ruscus aculeatus	Butcher's Broom	10
Sagina procumbens	Procumbent Pearlwort	1-11
Salix alba	White Willow	2 3 11
Salix aurita	Eared Willow	7
Salix caprea	Goat Willow	1-12
Salix cinerea	Grey Willow	1 10
Salix cinerea ssp. oleifolia	Grey Willow	3
Salix fragilis	Crack Willow	1 4 6 10-12
Salix purpurea	Purple Willow	4
Salix viminalis	Osier	2 3
Sambucus nigra	Elder	1-12
Sambucus racemosa	Red-berried Elder	10
Sanguisorba minor ssp. minor	Salad Burnet	2 3 11
Sanguisorba officinalis	Great Burnet	2 3
Sanicula europaea	Sanicle	1-3 7
Saponaria officinalis	Soapwort	square U2 only
Scilla siberica	Siberian Squill	10
Scrophularia auriculata	Water Figwort	1-4 6-8 10 111
Scrophularia nodosa	Common Figwort	1-12
Scrophularia vernalis	Yellow Figwort	10 11
Scutellaria galericulata	Skullcap	3-5
Sedum acre	Biting Stonecrop	10
Sedum album	White Stonecrop	10
Sedum anglicum	English Stonecrop	2-10
Senecio erucifolius	Hoary Ragwort	1-6 8-10
Senecio jacobaea	Common Ragwort	1-8 10 11
Senecio sylvaticus	Heath Groundsel	7
Senecio viscosus	Sticky Groundsel	1-3 5 8 10 11
Senecio vulgaris	Groundsel	1-12
Sequoia sempervirens	Coast Redwood	7
Sequoiadendron giganteum	Wellingtonia	10
Serratula tinctoria	Saw-wort	2 3 7-9
Sherardia arvensis	Field Madder	3
Silaum silaus	Pepper Saxifrage	2 3
Silene dioica	Red Campion	1-11
Silene latifolia	White Campion	1-12
Silene vulgaris ssp. vulgaris	Bladder Campion	2
Silybum marianum	Milk Thistle	2
Sinapis alba	White Mustard	3
Sinapis arvensis	Charlock	2 3 8
Sisymbrium officinale	Hedge Mustard	1-12
Solanum dulcamara	Woody Nightshade	1-11
Solanum nigrum	Black Nightshade	4 7 11
Sonchus arvensis	Corn Sow-thistle	1-10 12
Sonchus asper	Prickly Sow-thistle	2 6 10 11
Sonchus oleraceus	Smooth Sow-thistle	1-6 10 12
Sorbus aria agg.	Whitebeam	6
Sorbus aucuparia	Rowan	1-4 6 7 10
Sorbus intermedia	Swedish Whitebeam	7
Sparganium erectum	Branched Bur-reed	3 4 11
Spergula arvensis	Corn Spurrey	11
Stachys officinalis	Betony	1-10
Stachys palustris	Marsh Woundwort	2
Stachys sylvatica	Hedge Woundwort	1-12
Stellaria graminea	Lesser Stitchwort	2-10
Stellaria holostea	Greater Stitchwort	1-12
Stellaria media	Common Chickweed	1-12
Stellaria uliginosa	Bog Stitchwort	square K3 only
Succisa pratensis	Devil's-bit Scabious	1-11

Symphoricarpos albus	Snowberry	1-3 5-7 10 11
Symphytum asperum	Rough Comfrey	only in arable records
Symphytum grandiflorum	Creeping Comfrey	11
Symphytum officinale	Common Comfrey	10 11
Tamus communis	Black Bryony	1-12
Tanacetum parthenium	Feverfew	2 10
Tanacetum vulgare	Tansy	2-4
Taraxacum aggregate	Dandelion	1-12
Taxus baccata	Yew	10
Thlaspi arvense	Common Pennycress	2 11
Tilia cordata	Small-leaved Lime	2 10
Tilia x europaea	Lime	1-7 10
Torilis japonica	Hedge Parsley	1-12
Trachystemon orientalis	Abraham-Isaac-Jacob	10
Tragopogon pratensis	Goat's-beard	1-6 9 11
Trifolium campestre	Hop Trefoil	1-3 5 7 9-11
Trifolium dubium	Lesser Yellow Trefoil	2 3 5-9
Trifolium fragiferum	Strawberry Clover	2 6
Trifolium hybridum	Alsike Clover	2
Trifolium medium	Zigzag Clover	2 7 9
Trifolium pratense	Red Clover	1-10
Trifolium repens	White Clover	1-12
Tripleurospermum inodorum	Scentless Mayweed	1 2 4 5 8-12
Tsuga heterophylla	Western Hemlock	5 6
Tussilago farfara	Colt's-foot	1-12
Ulex europaeus	Gorse	1-3 5 7
Ulmus glabra	Wych Elm	1-10
Ulmus minor	Small-leaved Elm	1 2 7
Ulmus procera	English Elm	1-12
Ulmus x vegeta	Huntington Elm	7
Urtica dioica	Stinging Nettle	1-12
Urtica urens	Small Nettle	4
Valeriana officinalis	Common Valerian	1-10
Valerianella locusta	Cornsalad	2 11
Verbascum phlomoides	Orange Mullein	10 11
Verbascum thapsus	Great Mullein	2 4 10 11
Veronica anagallis-aquatica	Blue Water Speedwell	10 11
Veronica arvensis	Wall Speedwell	1-4 6 7 9 10
Veronica beccabunga	Brooklime	1-8 10 12
Veronica catenata	Pink Water-speedwell	11
Veronica chamaedrys	Germander Speedwell	1-12
Veronica hederifolia	Ivy-leaved Speedwell	2
Veronica montana	Wood Speedwell	7
Veronica officinalis	Heath Speedwell	1-3 8
Veronica persica	Common Field Speedwell	2 3 7-11
Veronica serpyllifolia	Thyme-leaved Speedwell	1-12
Viburnum lantana	Wayfaring Tree	1-10
Viburnum opulus	Guelder-rose	1-12
Viburnum sargentii v. flavum	Guelder Rose	4
Vicia cracca	Tufted Vetch	1-4 6-9 11
Vicia hirsuta	Hairy Tare	2 3 9 11
Vicia sativa	Common Vetch	1-12
Vicia sepium	Bush Vetch	1-11
Vicia tetrasperma	Smooth Tare	2-9 11
Vinca minor	Lesser Periwinkle	10
Viola arvensis	Field Pansy	1-5 7 8 11
Viola canina	Heath Dog-violet	3
Viola hirta	Hairy Violet	1-3 8

Viola odorata	Sweet Violet	2 10 11
Viola reichenbachiana	Wood Dog Violet	1 2 7-10
Viola riviniana	Common Dog Violet	1-12
Viola tricolor	Wild Pansy	2
X Cupressocyparis leylandii	Leyland Cypress	2 5 6
Zannichellia palustris	Horned Pondweed	2 6

Grasses

Taxon	Vernacular	Sections
Agrostis canina sens. lat.	Brown Bent	1267
Agrostis capillaris	Common Bent	3
Agrostis stolonifera	Creeping Bent	123567
Alopecurus geniculatus	Marsh Foxtail	789
Alopecurus myosuroides	Slender Foxtail	27
Alopecurus pratensis	Meadow Foxtail	1-9
Anisantha sterilis	Barren Brome	237
Anthoxanthum odoratum	Sweet Vernal Grass	1-9
Arrhenatherum elatius	False Oat-Grass	1-9
Brachypodium pinnatum	Tor Grass	267
Brachypodium sylvaticum	False-brome	1-10
Briza media	Quaking-grass	236 11
Bromopsis erecta	Upright Brome	1-10
Bromopsis ramosa	Hairy Brome	1-9
Bromus commutatus	Meadow Brome	4
Bromus hordeaceus	Soft Brome	3
Bromus lepidus	Slender Soft Brome	7
Bromus racemosus	Smooth Brome	2
Calamagrostis canescens	Purple Small-reed	4
Calamagrostis epigejos	Bush Grass	1-10
Cynosurus cristatus	Crested Dog's-tail	235679
Dactylis glomerata	Cock's-foot	1-46-9
Danthonia decumbens	Heath Grass	3
Deschampsia cespitosa	Tufted Hair-grass	1-11
Elymus caninus var. caninus	Bearded couch	1267
Elytrigia repens	Common Couch	23679
Festuca arundinacea	Tall Fescue	1279
Festuca gigantea	Giant Fescue	1346-9
Festuca ovina	Sheep's Fescue	3
Festuca pratensis	Meadow Fescue	12369
F. pratensis x lolium perenne	Rye-grass (hybrid)	3
Festuca rubra agg.	Red Fescue	1236
Glyceria fluitans	Flote-grass	2579
Glyceria maxima	Reed Sweet-grass	2
Helictotrichon pratense	Meadow Oat-grass	3
Helictotrichon pubescens	Downy Oat-grass	23
Holcus lanatus	Yorkshire Fog	125-11
Holcus mollis	Creeping Soft Grass	2
Hordeum murinum	Wall Barley	2

Hordeum secalinum	Meadow Barley	2 11
Isolepis setacea	Bristle Club-rush	3
Lolium perenne	Common Rye-grass	3569 11
Melica uniflora	Wood Melick	2
Milium effusum	Wood Millet	28
Phalaris arundinacea	Reed Canary-grass	23 11
Phalaris minor	Lesser Canary-grass	7
Phleum bertolonii	Smaller Cat's-tail	23
Phleum pratense	Timothy	29
Phragmites australis	Common Reed	34
Poa annua	Annual Meadow-grass	1-4 6-9
Poa compressa	Flattened Meadow-grass	2
Poa nemoralis	Wood Meadow-grass	126-9
Poa pratensis sens. lat.	Smooth Meadow-grass	123679
Poa trivialis	Rough Meadow-grass	236-9
Trisetum flavescens	Yellow Oat-grass	2369
Vulpia bromoides	Squirrel-tail Fescue	3
Vulpia myuros	Rat's-tail Fescue	237

Sedge

Carex acutiformis	Lesser Pond Sedge	234 10
Carex caryophyllea	Spring Sedge	3
Carex divulsa subsp. divulsa	Grey Sedge	1269
Carex flacca	Glaucous Sedge	1-9
Carex hirta	Hairy Sedge	1-9
Carex otrubae	False Fox Sedge	1-9
Carex ovalis	Oval Sedge	1-7
Carex panicea	Carnation Sedge	34
Carex pendula	Pendulous Sedge	1-12
Carex remota	Remote Sedge	1-9
Carex riparia	Great Pond Sedge	1-5 7-10
Carex spicata	Spiked Sedge	23679
Carex strigosa	Thin-spiked Wood Sedge	27
Carex sylvatica	Wood Sedge	1-10
Cyperus longus	Galingale (intro)	2
Eleocharis palustris	Common Spike-rush	346
Isolepis setacea	Bristle Club-rush	3
Juncus acutiflorus	Sharp-flowered Rush	29
Juncus articulatus	Jointed Rush	1-12
Juncus bufonius sens. lat.	Toad Rush	1-10
Juncus conglomeratus	Compact Rush	1-12
Juncus effusus	Soft Rush	1-12
Juncus inflexus	Hard Rush	1-12
Luzula campestris	Good Friday Grass	1346 10
Luzula multiflora	Heath Woodrush	239
Luzula pilosa	Hairy Woodrush	79
Schoenoplectus lacustris	Bulrush	2347 10
Typha angustifolia	Lesser Reed Mace	34

Typha latifolia	Greater Reed Mace	1-4 7 10-12

Fungi

Abortiporus biennis	Bkt.	6
Agaricus augustus		2
" silvicola	Wood Mushroom	2-57
" sylvaticus		58
Agrocybe erebia		3
Alatospora acuminata		2
Aleuria aurantia		3
Amanita citrina	False Death Cap	8
" fulva		8
" phalloides	Death Cap	35
" rubescens	Blusher	23
Anguillospora crassa		2
" longissima		2
Anthracobia melaloma	disc type	2
Arcyria cinerea		2
Armillaria mellea	Honey Fungus	1-10
" polymyces	" "	6
Arrhenia spathulata		5
Arthrobotrys conoides		6
Ascobolus albidus		2
" crenulatus		2
" immersus		6
" stictoideus		26
Ascocoryne sarcoides		23
Athelia arachnoidea		6
Auricularia auricula-judae	Jews Ear	1-12
" mesenterica	Tripe Fungus	345
Auriscalpium vulgare		26
Baeospora myosura		28
Bisporella citrina	yellow disc type	3
Blumeria graminis		2
Bolbitius vitellinus	Yellow Cowpat Tstool	1-7 12
Boletus badius		25
" edulis	Cep	3
" luridus		2
" porosporus		35
Botryobasidium aureum		5
Bovista plumbea	Puff-ball	3
Bulgaria inquinans	Popes Buttons	123
Calocera cornea		1-9
" pallidospathulata		6
" viscosa		1-12
Calvatia excipuliformis	Puff-ball	1347
Ceratiomyxa fruticulosa		6
Chaetosphaerella pnaeostroma		2
Cheilymenia raripila		2
" theleboloides	disc type	6
Chlorosplenium aeruginascens	Green Wood-cup	1-79
Chroogomphus rutilus		6
Circinotrichum maculiforme		6
Clavaria argillacea	Field Club	3
Clavariadelphus fistulosus		36
Clavariopsis aquatica		2
Claviceps purpurea	Ergot	29
Clavulina cinerea	Grey Coral	357

" cristata	Coral	2-7
Clavulinopsis corniculata		36
" helvola		3
Clitocybe flaccida	Tawny Funnel Cap	3-9
" fragrans		12357
" geotropa		1-8 12
" gigantea		346
" hydrogramma		3
" infundibuliformis	Funnel Cap	3
" nebularis	Clouded Agaric	57
" odora	Aniseed T'stool	1456
" phyllophila		3
" sauveolens		6
Coleosporium sp.	rust	1
Colletotrichum dematium		6
Collybia butyracea	Butter Cap	578
" dryophila		56
" fusipes	Spindle Foot	236
" maculata	Spotted Tough-shank	67
Comayricha nigra		6
Coprinus atramentarius	Com. Ink Cap	347
" comatus	Shaggy Ink Cap	1-12
" disseminatus	Fairies Bonnet	1-7 12
" heptemerus		26
" lagopus		357
" micaceus	Glistening Ink Cap	1
" plicatilis		23
" stercoreus		2
Coriolus versicolor	Bkt.	1-12
Cortinarius armillatus		3
" crocolitus		2
" pholideus		2
" purpurascens		5
Crepidotus luteolus		5
" variabilis		13
Cribraria aurantiaca		6
" persoonii		6
Crocicreas cyathoideum		5
Cyanthus striatus	Birds Nest	2
Cylindrobasidium evolvens	Bkt.	3
Cystoderma amianthinum		5
Dacrymyces stillatus	jelly type	1-6
Daedalea quercina	Maze-gill	239
Daedaleopsis confragosa	Blushing Bkt.	2-7
Daldinia concentrica	Cramp Balls	1-9 12
Dasyscyphus brevipilosum		2
Diatrype disciformis	Black Spot	3679
" quercina		5
" stigma		2
Dictyosporium toruloides		2
Diplococcium spicatum		6
Disciotis venosa	cup type	1
Doratomyces microsporus		2
" nanus		2
Encoelia furfuracea	cup type	2-6
Endophragmiella pallescens		5
Entoloma conferendum		12
" farinolens		3
" sericeum		<u>12</u>

Epichloe typhina		2
Erysiphe biocellata		6
" cichoracearum		6
" cruciferarum		6
" cynoglossi		6
" depressa		6
" heraclei		6
" hypericacearum		5
" sordida		6
Excipularia fusispora		6
Exidia glandulosa	Witches Butter	2-7
" truncata		5
Flammulina velutipes	Velvet Shank	1-10 12
Fomes fomentarius	Hoof Fungus	3
Fuligo septica		6
" " var. flava		6
Fusidium aeruginosum		56
Galerina laevis		2
" mutabilis		56
" pumila		5
Ganoderma adspersum		6
" applanatum	Tinder Fungus	3
" lucidum		3
Gymnopilus penetrans		12589
Hebeloma leucosarx		15
" sinapizans		25
Helicondendron tubulosum		6
Heliscella stellata		2
Helminthosporium sp.		2
Helvella crispa	White Helvella	567
Heterobasidion annosum	Root Fomes	26
Heteroconium tetracoilum		2
Hohenbuehelia petaloides		23
Hormotheca robertiani		2
Hyaloscypha stevensonii		6
Hygrocybe ceracea	Wax Cap	3
" conica	Wax Cap	23
" marchii		3
" nigrescens		23
" psittacina	Parrot Wax Cap	3
" subglobispora		3
Hygrophoropsis aurantiaca	False Chanterelle	1-8
Hymenoscyphus fructigenus	Nut Cap	236
Hyphodontia sambuci	White Mould	3
Hypholoma capnoides		356
" fasciculare	Sulphur Tuft	1-10 12
" marginatum		5
" sublateritium	Brick Cap	238
Hypocrea pulvinata		2
Hypomyces aurantius		2
Hypoxylon fragiforme	Orange Spot	3
" multiforme		6
Inocybe actua		6
" fastigiata		25
" geophylla		2
" maculata		25
" pusio		6

" sindonia		6
Inonotus dryadeus		6
Idophanus carneus		2
Laccaria amethystina	Amethyst Deceiver	1-8
" bicolor		6
" laccata	Deceiver	1-8
Lachnella villosa		6
Lachnellula occidentalis		2
Lacrymaria velutina	Weeping Widow	16
Lactarius fuliginosus	Milk-cap	27
" hepaticus		2
" mitissimus		27
" pallidus		2
" quietus		
" rufus	Rufus Milk-cap	6
" vellereus	Fleecy Milk-cap	23
Langermannia gigantea	Giant Puffball	2
Lasiobolus papillatus		6
Lasiophaeria hirsuta		5
Lecanora conizaeoides		2
Leccinum scabrum	Brown Birch Bolete	5
Lentinellus cochleatus	Funnel Cap	12
Leocarpus fragilis	Brittle Smooth-fruit	23
Lepiota cristata		7
" friesii		2
" grangei		3
" hystrix		5
" procera	Parasol	8
" rhacodes	Shaggy Parasol	2578
Lepista nuda	Wood Blewit	2-8
" saeva	Field Blewit	3
Leptosphaeria agnita		5
Lycoperdon epidendron	Wolves Milk	2-6
" foetidum	Puff-ball	2
" perlatum	"	1-10 12
" pyriforme	"	1-9
Marasmius oreades	Fairy Ring Champignon	345
" ramealis		123567
Melamspora caprearum		5
" populnea		6
Melampsoridium betulinum		5
Melanoleuca arcuata		3
" cinerascens		3
Melastiza chateri		8
Menispora ciliata		26
Meripilus giganteus		6
Meruliopsis corium		5
Merulius tremellosus		3
Microsphaera alphitoides	Mildew	156
" hypericacearum	"	6
Mitrophora semilibera	Morel	127
Mucilago crustacea	Slime Mould	2
Mutinus caninus	Dog Stinkhorn	2
Mycena alcalina		23
" clavularis		2
" epipterygia		2
" galericulata		257
" galopus		2
" inclinata		356

Species	Common name	Ref
" melaleuca		2
" metata		2
" polygramma		3
" speira		2
" tintinnabulum		2
Mycoacia uda		6
Myaxarium subhyalinum		6
Nectria cinnabarina	Coral Spot	1-12
" magnusiana	" "	1-10 12
Neobulgaria pura		3
Nolanea farinolens		3
" staurospora		3
Oncopodiella trigonella		6
Orbilia xanthostigma		2
Otidea bufonia	Cup	2
Oudemansiella radicata	Rooting Shank	67
Oxyporus populinus	Bkt.	36
Panaeolus acuminatus		3
Paxillus atrotomentosus		8
" involutus	Brown Roll-rim	123578
Penicillium brevicompactum		6
Peziza aurantia	Orange Peel	2
" badia	Cup	278
" echinospora	"	1
" praetervisa		7
" vesiculosa		67
Phaeohelotium subcarneum		6
Phaeoisaria clematidis		6
Phallus impudicus	Stinkhorn	1-10
Phlebia merismoides		3
" radiata		5
Pholiota squarrosa	Shaggy Pholiota	5 12
Phragmidium mucronatum		2
Physarum leucophaeum		6
Pilobolus crystallinus		26
" kleinii		6
Piptocephalis repens		6
Piptoporus betulinus	Razor Strop	1-12
Pleurotus cornucopiae		3
" ostreatus	Oyster Mushroom	13459
Pluteus cervinus		1
" nanus		1
" romellii		2
" salicinus		6
Poculum firmum		5
Podospora sectosa		6
Polydesmia pruinosa		25
Polyporus badius		123
" brumalis		2
" ciliatus		23
" squamosa	Dryads Saddle	2-7 10 12
" varius		1
Psathyrella candolleana		36
" hydrophila		37
" marcescibilis		3
" multipedata		2
" spadiceo-grisea		25
Pseudotomentella tristis		6

Pseudotrametes gibbosa		36
Psilocybe crobula		2
Puccinia brachypodii	Rust	2
" caricina v. ribesii-pendulae		6
" glechomatis		26
" poarum		5
" punctiformis		26
Reticularia lycoperdon	Bark Puff-ball	2-6
Rhizina undulata	Pine Fire Fungus	7
Rhytisma acerinum	Tar Spot	1-6
Rigidoporus sanguinolentus		1
" ulmarius		278
Russula atropurpurea	Blackish-purple Russula	6
" delica	Milk White Russula	8
" emetica	The Sickener	56
" foetens		2
" fragilis	Fragile Russula	56
" lepida		6
" luteotacta		7
" nitida		3
" ochroleuca	Yellow Russula	5-8
" sanguinea		5
" xerampelina	Green Russula	56
Rustroemia firms		6
Sarcoscphyla coccinea	Scarlet Elf Cup	29
Sawadaea bicornis		56
" tulasnei	Mildew	10
Schizophyllum commune	Split Gill	36
Schizothecium tetrasporum		2
" vesticola		2
Scleroderma areolatum	Puff-ball	36
" citrinum	Earth Ball	3
" verrucosum	Puff-ball	6
Scopuloides hydnoides		6
Scutellinia scutellata	Eyelash Fungus	346
" umbrorum		2
Sebacina incrustans		7
Skeletocutis nivea		6
Sparassis crispa	Cauliflower Fungus	3
Sphaerotheca fugax		2
" fusca		26
" pannosa		25
Spinellus fusiger		25
Sporidesmium folliculatum		2
Stemonitis fusca		6
Stereum hirsutum	Hairy Stereum	1-478
" rugosum	Bkt.	23
" sanguinolentum		5
Stilbella fimetaria		6
Stropharia aeruginosa	Verdigris Agaric	123567
" caerulea		15
" coronilla		6
" pseudocyanea		2
" semiglobata	Dung Roundhead	6
Stypella vermiformis		6
Suillas granulatus	Boletus	23
" grevillei	Larch Boletus	356
Symphytocarpus flaccidus		6

Tarzetta catinus		3
Tetracladium marchalianum		2
" setigerum		2
Thelebolus nanus		2
Thelephora anthocephala		6
" palmata	Brown Coral	5
" terrestris	Carpet Fungus	5
Trametes gibbosa		23
" hirsuta		2
Tremella globospora		2
" mesenterica	Yellow Brain	1-12
Trichaptum abietinum		6
Trichobolus zuckalii		2
Trichoderma viride		5
Tricholoma cingulatum		2
" fulvum		7
" terreum		2
" virgatum		7
Tricholomopsis rutilans	Plums and Custard	24567
Trichophaea hemisphaerioides	Cup	2
Tricladium angulatum		2
Tromyces stipticus		3
Tryomyces caesius	Bkt.	58
" ptychogaster		5
" stipticus	Bkt.	57
Tubaria furfuracea	Cup	1235
Tubeufia cerea		2
Tubifera ferruginosa	Slime Mould	6
Tulasnella sp.		6
Typhula erythropus		3
" setipes		13
Ustilago avenae		2
" hordei	Barley Smut	2
" violacea		2
Vascellum pratense	Puff-ball	6
Verpa conica	Morell	12
Volucrispora graminea		2
Volvariella speciosa		26
Vuilleminia sp.		2
Xylaria hypoxylon	Candle Snuff	1-12
" polymorpha	Dead Mans Fingers	23

Bryophytes

Alonia aloides var. aloides	11
Amblystegium riparium	13458 10
" serpens var. serpens	1-8 10 11 12
" varium	2
Anomodon viticulosus	12
Atrichum undulatum var. undulatum	1-8
" " var.minus	2
Aulacomnium androgynum	2-7 12
Barbula convulata var.commutata	3 10
Barbula convulata var. convulata	13
" fallax	368 11
" hornschuchiana	34 10
" recurvirostra	4

"	tophacea	11
"	trifaria	<u>12</u>
"	unguiculata	1-11
"	vinealis	4 10
Brachythecium albicans		34 11
"	glareosum	4
"	populeum	348
"	rivulare	7 12
"	rutabulum	1-12
"	salebrosum	7
"	velutinum	1346 10
Bryum argenteum		1-12
"	" var. lanatum	348
"	bicolor	24-11
"	caespiticium	28 10
"	capillare	1-4679-12
"	dunanse	11
"	flaccidum	2347 10 12
"	klinggraeffii	6 12
"	pseudotriquetrum	349
"	radiculosum	46 10 12
"	rubens	26-11
"	ruderale	10
"	torquescens	3
Calliergon cuspidatum		1-12
Campylopus introflexus		2-79
"	paradoxus	3479
Campylium chrysophyllum		3
"	stellatum	34
Ceratodon purureus		1-47-11
Cirriphyllum crassinervium		79 10 12
"	piliferum	1-46-8 10
Cratoneuron commutatum		<u>12</u>
"	filicinum	2-7 10 12
Cryphaea heteromalla		<u>12</u>
Ctenidium molluscum		34
Dicranella heteromalla		1-9 11
"	schreberana	36
"	staphylina	8 10
"	varia	369 10 11
Dicranoweisia cirrata		1-79 10 12
Dicranum scoparium		3457
"	tauricum	2
Drepanocladus aduncus		34
Eurhynchium praelongum		1-12
"	pumilum	369 10 12
"	speciosum	4
"	striatum	1-7 12
"	swartzii var. swartzii	1-8 10-12
"	" var. rigidum	3 11
Fissidens bryoides		2
"	exilis	34 10
"	incurvus	346
"	pusillus	6
"	taxifolius	1-11
"	viridulus	6
Fontinalis antipyretica		34 10
Funaria hygrometrica		1-4678 10 11
Grimmia pulvinata		234678 10
Herzogiella seligeri		7
Homalia trichomanoides		24 10 12

Homalothecium sericeum	259-12
Hylocomium splendens	4
Hypnum cupressiforme var. cupressiforme	1-12
" " var. lacunosum	1-467 10 11
" " var. resupinatum	1-8 10
Isopterygium elegans	68
Isothecium myosuroides	3479 12
" myurum	37 10 12
Leptobryum pyriforme	6
Leskea polycarpa	10
Mnium hornum	1-8
" stellare	2
Neckera complanata	2 10 12
Orthodontium lineare	2-79 10
Orthotrichum affine	1-10 12
" anomalum	3
" diaphanum	1-468-10 12
" lyellii	48
" pulchellum	<u>12</u>
" tenellum	<u>12</u>
Oxystegus sinuosus	10 12
Phascum cuspidatum	269 10 12
" floerkeanum	6
Phsycomitrium pyriforme	6 10
Plagiomnium affine	234679 10
" elatum	<u>12</u>
" rostratum	2356 12
" undulatum	1-10 12
Plagiothecium curvifolium	1-467
" denticulatum	1-79 10
" nemorale	2346-9
Pleuridium acuminatum	6
Pohlia carnea	36
" nutans	34 12
" wahlenbergia	3478
Polytrichum commune	4
" formosum	3458
" juniperinum	34
" piliferum	34
Pottia truncata	268 10
Pseudoscleropodium purum	2-6 11
Pterygoneurum ovatum	<u>12</u>
Rhizomnium punctatum	14-79 12
Rhynchostegiella tenella	10 12
Rhynchostegium confertum	1-68-10 12
" murale	24
" riparioides	26 10 12
Rhytidiadelphus squarrosus	2-7 10 11 12
" triquestrus	2
Schistidium apocarpum var. apocarpum	234 10 11
Tetraphis pellucida	3-7
Thamnobryum alopecurum	2-10 12
Thuidium tamariscinum	1-8
Tortula intermedia	2 10
" laevipila	10 12
" latifolia	10
" muralis	2-468 10 11 12
" ruralis	48 10 12
" viriscens	<u>12</u>
Ulota crispa var. crispa	37
" " var. norvegica	459 12

" phyllantha	9
Zygodon conoideus	10 12
" viridissimus	2 10 12

Liverworts

Aneura pinguis	46
Conocephalum conicum	2 10 12
Frulliana dilatata	346
" tamarisci	<u>12</u>
Lepidozia reptans	3
Lophocolea bipendata/cuspidata	1-11
" heterophylla	1-9 11
Lunularia cruciata	10
Marchantia polymorpha	3
Metzgeria furcata	2-5
" fruticulosa	<u>12</u>
Pellia endiviifolia	236 10 12
Plagiochila asplenioides	2-689
Porella platyphylla	10
Ptilidium pulcherrimum	6
Radula complanata	2
Riccardia chamaedrifolia	3 11
Ricciocarpus natans	34

Algae

Chara globularis globularis	Stonewort	34
Chara hispida v. major	Stonewort	34
Chara virgata	Stonewort	34
Nostoc commune		234

LEPIDOPTERA

Code	Taxon	Vernacular	Sections

Butterflies

Code	Taxon	Vernacular	Sections
1593	Aglais urticae	Small Tortoiseshell	1-12
1553	Anthocharis cardamines	Orange Tip	1-12
1629	Aphantopus hyperantus	Ringlet	1-9 12
1572	Aricia agestis	Brown Argus	12456 10 11
1555	Callophrys rubi	Green Hairstreak	2
1580	Celastrina argiolus	Holly Blue	2-578 10 12
1627	Coenonympha pamphilus	Small Heath	1-12
1545	Colias croceus	Clouded Yellow	234
1532	Erynnis tages	Dinghy Skipper	234
1546	Gonepteryx rhamni	Brimstone	1-12
1597	Inachis io	Peacock	1-12
1584	Ladoga camilla	White Admiral	2-7
1615	Lasiommata megera	Wall	37
1541	Leptidea sinapis	Wood White	2-9
1561	Lycaena phlaeas	Small Copper	1-11
	" " ab caeruleopunctata	" "	24
1626	Maniola jurtina	Meadow Brown	1-12
1620	Melanargia galathea	Marbled White	2-6 11
1531	Ochlodes venata	Large Skipper	1-12
1614	Pararge aegeria	Speckled Wood	1-12
1549	Pieris brassicae	Large White	1-12
1551	Pieris napi	Green Veined White	1-12
1550	Pieris rapae	Small White	1-12
1598	Polygonia c-album	Comma	1-12
1574	Polyommatus icarus	Com. Blue	1-12
1534	Pyrgus malvae	Grizzled Skipper	234678
1625	Pyronia tithonus	Gatekeeper/Hedge Brown	1-12
1557	Quercusia quercus	Purple Hairstreak	1-7 10 12
1559	Strymonidia pruni	Black Hairstreak	23
1558	Strymonidia w-album	White-letter Hairstreak	145
1527	Thymelicus lineola	Essex Skipper	1-5
1526	Thymelicus sylvestris	Small Skipper	1-12
1590	Vanessa atalanta	Red Admiral	1-12
1591	Vanessa cardui	Painted Lady	1-12

Macro-moths

Code	Vernacular	Sections recorded
14	Ghost Moth	1-7 9 11
15	Orange Swift	4 7 9 11
16	Gold Swift	2 7
17	Common Swift	1-9 11
161	Leopard Moth	2-6 8
162	Goat Moth	2 3
169	Six-spot Burnet	2-5
170	Five-spot Burnet	2-5
370	Hornet Moth	2346 Q1
371	Lunar Hornet Moth	5
378	Orange-tailed Clearwing	5 7
1631	December Moth	5 7 8
1632	Pale Eggar	3 4
1634	Lackey	1-9

1637	Oak Eggar	3 7 9
1638	Fox Moth	3
1640	Drinker	1-10
1642	Lappet	2 3
1643	Emperor	2 4 5
1645	Scalloped Hook-tip	1-7 9
1646	Oak Hook-tip	1-9 11
1648	Pebble Hook-tip	1-7 9
1651	Chinese Character	1-4 6-9 11
1652	Peach Blossom	1-9
1653	Buff Arches	1-10
1654	Figure of Eighty	1 3-7 9
1655	Poplar Lutestring	2-7
1657	Common Lutestring	4
1658	Oak Lutestring	2 4-7
1659	Yellow Horned	2-7
1660	Frosted Green	1-3 7-9 11
1661	Orange Underwing	2-5
1663	March Moth	1-8
1666	Large Emerald	2-8
1667	Blotched Emerald	1-8
1669	Common Emerald	1-9
1673	Small Emerald	1 2 4 5 7 9
1674	Little Emerald	2 4 7 8 9
1679	False Mocha	7
1680	Maiden's Blush	2-9
1682	Blood-vein	1-11
1690	Small Blood-vein	2 8 11
1692	Lesser Cream Wave	1 3 7
1693	Cream Wave	1 2 4-7 9
1702	Small Fan-footed Wave	1-9 11
1705	Dwarf Cream Wave	2 4 7 8 9
1708	Single-dotted Wave	1-9 11
1709	Satin Wave	4
1712	Small Scallop	2 8
1713	Riband Wave	1-9 11
1715	Plain Wave	1-8
1716	Vestal	2 4
1722	Flame Carpet	3 4 6 8
1724	Red Twin-spot Carpet	1-11
1725	Dark-barred Twin-spot Carpet	1 6 8
1726	Large Twin-spot Carpet	1-4 6-10
1727	Silver-ground Carpet	1-9 11
1728	Garden Carpet	4-8 11
1732	Shaded Broad-bar	1-11
1738	Common Carpet	1 2 4-9 11
1739	Wood Carpet	1 2 3 5 6 8
1742	Yellow Shell	1 2 3 5 7-11
1745	Mallow	2 3
1746	Shoulder Stripe	1-9
1747	Streamer	1 3-7 9 11
1748	Beautiful Carpet	1-7 9
1750	Water Carpet	1-9
1752	Purple Bar	1 3-9
1754	Phoenix	5 6 7
1755	Chevron	2 4 6 8
1756	Northern Spinach	1
1757	Spinach	10
1758	Barred Straw	1-7 9 10
1759	Small Phoenix	1-9
1760	Red-green Carpet	2 4 7

1762	Dark Marbled Carpet	1-7 9
1764	Common Marbled Carpet	1-9
1765	Barred Yellow	1-9
1766	Blue-bordered Carpet	4
1768	Grey Pine Carpet	1 2 4-9
1769	Spruce Carpet	1 2 4-9
1773	Broken-barred Carpet	1 2 4-7 9
1776	Green Carpet	1-11
1777	July Highflyer	1-11
1778	May Highflyer	4 7
1781	Small Waved Umber	1 2 4 5
1782	Fern	1 2 4 5
1784	Pretty Chalk Carpet	1 2 5 7
1789	Scallop Shell	3 4
1790	Tissue	6
1791	Brown Scallop	2-5 9 10
1792	Dark Umber	7 8
1795	November Moth	1 2 4 7
1796	Pale November Moth	1 5 7
1797	Autumnal Moth	2-7
1799	Winter Moth	2-5 7 8
1800	Northern Winter Moth	4 5 8
1803	Small Rivulet	2-7 9 10
1804	Barred Rivulet	7 9
1807	Grass Rivulet	7
1808	Sandy Carpet	2 6
1809	Twin-spot Carpet	4 5 10
1811	Slender Pug	1-5 8-11
1812	Maple Pug	5 6
1813	Haworth's Pug	1 2 5
1815	Cloaked Pug	5
1816	Toadflax Pug	8
1819	Mottled Pug	1-7 9
1825	Lime-speck Pug	1 2 4 5 7 8 9 11
1826	Triple-spotted Pug	1 4
1828	Satyr Pug	3 7
1830	Wormwood Pug	2 3 5 6 8 11
1834	Common Pug	1 2 4-9
1835	White-spotted Pug	1 2 4-9
1836	Campanula Pug	8
1837	Grey Pug	1-9
1838	Tawny-speckled Pug	4 9 11
1839	Bordered Pug	5
1842	Plain Pug	8
1844	Ochreous Pug	2 5-8
1846	Narrow-winged Pug	5
1849	Ash Pug	4 6
1852	Brindled Pug	1-9 11
1853	Oak-tree Pug	1 4-7 9
1856	Larch Pug	2 7
1857	Dwarf Pug	2 5 6
1858	V-Pug	1 3-7
1859	Sloe Pug	2 3 4
1860	Green Pug	1-10
1862	Double-striped Pug	1 3 5 7 8 9
1867	Treble Bar	2 4
1870	Chimney Sweeper	2 3
1875	Small White Wave	2 4-7
1876	Small Yellow Wave	1 2 3 9
1879	Seraphim	4-7
1883	Yellow-barred Brindle	2 4

1884	Magpie Moth	1-9 11
1887	Clouded Border	1-9
1888	Scorched Carpet	2 4
1893	Tawny-barred Angle	2 3 5 7 8 9
1894	Latticed Heath	2-9 11
1902	Brown Silver-line	4
1904	Scorched Wing	1-7 9
1906	Brimstone Moth	1-11
1907	Bordered Beauty	2 5 6 7 9
1910	Lilac Beauty	2 3 5
1912	August Thorn	3 4
1913	Canary-shouldered Thorn	3 5 6 7
1914	Dusky Thorn	2-7
1915	September Thorn	5 6 7 9
1917	Early Thorn	1-9
1919	Purple Thorn	1 3-9 11
1920	Scalloped Hazel	1 2 4-7 9
1921	Scalloped Oak	1-9
1922	Swallow-tailed Moth	1-10
1923	Feathered Thorn	3 4 5 7 8
1925	Small Brindled Beauty	2-7
1926	Pale Brindled Beauty	4 6 7
1927	Brindled Beauty	1-4 7
1930	Oak Beauty	1-9
1931	Peppered Moth	1-9
1931	Peppered Moth (melanic)	1 3-7
1932	Spring Usher	3-7
1933	Scarce Umber	3 4 5
1934	Dotted Border	2-8
1935	Mottled Umber	2 3 4 6 7
1936	Waved Umber	1-7 9 11
1937	Willow Beauty	1-9
1940	Satin Beauty	9
1941	Mottled Beauty	1-10
1944	Pale Oak Beauty	2-8
1947	Engrailed	1-9
1948	Small Engrailed	3-7
1950	Brindled White-spot	1-7
1951	Grey Birch	4 6 7
1952	Common Heath	3 4
1954	Bordered White	2 5 7 9
1955	Common White Wave	1-9
1956	Common Wave	1-9
1957	White-pinion Spotted	1-8
1958	Clouded Silver	1-9
1960	Early Moth	2 3 4
1961	Light Emerald	1-10
1962	Barred Red	2 3 5 8 9 11
1978	Pine Hawk-moth	2 5 6 8
1979	Lime Hawk-moth	4 6 7 8
1980	Eyed Hawk-moth	2 4 6 8 9
1981	Poplar Hawk-moth	1-9
1991	Elephant Hawk-moth	2-9
1994	Buff-tip	2-9
1995	Puss Moth	2 4
1997	Sallow Kitten	2 4 5 7 9 11
1998	Poplar Kitten	4 5 6 9
2000	Iron Prominent	2-9 11
2003	Pebble Prominent	1-9 11
2006	Lesser Swallow Prominent	2-6 9
2007	Swallow Prominent	1-7 9

2008	Coxcomb Prominent	1-9
2009	Maple Prominent	1-5 7 8
2010	Scarce Prominent	1 3 4
2011	Pale Prominent	1-9
2014	Marbled Brown	2 7
2015	Lunar Marbled Brown	1 4 5 7 9
2019	Chocolate-tip	3 5 6 7
2020	Figure of Eight	2-7
2026	Vapourer	1-9
2028	Pale Tussock	1-8
2030	Yellow-tail	1-9 11
2031	White Satin	4 6 7
2033	Black Arches	3 5-9
2035	Round-winged Muslin	7
2038	Muslin Footman	10
2044	Dingy Footman	1-9
2047	Scarce Footman	2-9 11
2049	Buff Footman	2 4 5 6 8 9
2050	Common Footman	1-9 11
2057	Garden Tiger	3-6 9
2060	White Ermine	1-7 9
2061	Buff Ermine	1-4 6 7 9
2063	Muslin Moth	7
2064	Ruby Tiger	1-9 11
2069	Cinnabar	2 3 4 8 11
2077	Short-cloaked Moth	3 4 5 8
2078	Least Black Arches	1-8
2082	Garden Dart	9
2087	Turnip Moth	2-6 8 9
2089	Heart and Dart	1-10
2091	Dark Sword-grass	2 4 5
2092	Shuttle Shaped Dart	2 3 5 7 9 11
2098	Flame	1-10
2102	Flame Shoulder	1-11
2105	Dotted Rustic	2 4 5
2107	Large Yellow Underwing	1-11
2109	Lesser Yellow Underwing	1-9 11
2110	Broad-b'dd Yellow Underwing	1-9
2111	Lesser Broad-b'dd Yellow U'wing	1-9 11
2112	Least Yellow Underwing	1-9
2114	Double Dart	1 5 8 9
2120	Ingrailed Clay	1-9
2122	Purple Clay	1-7
2123	Small Square-spot	1-9
2126	Setaceous Hebrew Character	1-9 11
2128	Double Square-spot	1-11
2133	Six-striped Rustic	2-8
2134	Square-spot Rustic	2-9
2136	Gothic	4
2138	Green Arches	3-6 8 9
2139	Red Chestnut	1-7
2145	Nutmeg	4 7 11
2150	Grey Arches	3-7 9
2154	Cabbage Moth	2 11
2155	Dot Moth	1-5 8
2157	Light Brocade	4
2158	Pale-shouldered Brocade	1 2 4-7 9
2160	Bright-line Brown-eye	1-11
2163	Broom Moth	2
2171	Marbled Coronet	2
2176	Antler	3 4 6 7

2178	Feathered Gothic	6 7
2179	Pine Beauty	1 5-9 11
2182	Small Quaker	1-8
2183	Blossom Underwing	2 4 6
2185	Lead-coloured Drab	1 2 4 5 6
2186	Powdered Quaker	4 6 7
2187	Common Quaker	1-9 11
2188	Clouded Drab	1-7 9 11
2189	Twin-spotted Quaker	3-9
2190	Hebrew Character	1-9 11
2192	Brown-line Bright-eye	2 4 5 8 11
2193	Clay	1-9 11
2197	Southern Wainscot	2 5 11
2198	Smoky Wainscot	1-11
2199	Common Wainscot	1-9 11
2205	Shoulder-striped Wainscot	2 3 5 7
2214	Chamomile Shark	1
2216	Shark	8
2221	Mullein	2
2225	Minor Shoulder-knot	1-7 9
2231	Deep-brown Dart	1 2 6 7
2232	Black Rustic	1 4 5 7
2237	Grey Shoulder-knot	3 4 6 7 8
2240	Blair's Shoulder-knot	7 8
2243	Early Grey	1-7 9
2245	Green-brindled Crescent	1-7
2247	Merveille du Jour	2 4 7
2248	Brindled Green	1 4 7 8
2252	Large Ranunculus	2
2256	Satellite	2-8
2258	Chestnut	2-8
2259	Dark Chestnut	1 5 7 8
2262	Brick	1-4 7 8 9
2263	Red-line Quaker	3 7
2264	Yellow-line Quaker	1-4 7
2265	Flounced Chestnut	2 4 7
2266	Brown-spot Pinion	1 2 5 7
2267	Beaded Chestnut	1 3 7 9
2269	Centre-barred Sallow	1-4 6 7 9
2270	Lunar Underwing	1 3 4 6 7
2271	Orange Sallow	2 6
2272	Barred Sallow	1 2 4 5 7 9
2273	Pink-barred Sallow	1 2 4 7 9
2274	Sallow	1 2 4 6 7 8
2278	Poplar Grey	1-9
2279	Sycamore	2 3 4 8
2280	Miller	3-8
2281	Alder Moth	2 4 7
2283	Dark Dagger	6
2284	Grey Dagger	1 3-10
2289	Knot Grass	4 7 8
2293	Marbled Beauty	1 2 3 6 7 11
2297	Copper Underwing	1-7 9 11
2298	Svensson's Copper Underwing	2 6 9
2299	Mouse Moth	1-9 11
2302	Brown Rustic	1-9
2303	Straw Underwing	1-3 5 6 8 9 11
2305	Small Angle Shades	1-6 8 9
2306	Angle Shades	1-9 11 12
2312	Olive	1-6 11
2313	Angle-striped Sallow	6

2318	Dun-bar	1-9 11
2319	Lunar-spotted Pinion	1 3 4 5 7
2321	Dark Arches	1-9 11
2322	Light Arches	1 3-9
2326	Clouded-bordered Brindle	1-9
2327	Clouded Brindle	4 5 7 9
2330	Dusky Brocade	3-6 8
2331	Small Clouded Brindle	5
2333	Large Nutmeg	1-10
2334	Rustic Shoulder-knot	2-9
2335	Slender Brindle	1 3-7
2336	Double Lobed	5
2337	Marbled Minor	1-10
2338	Rufous Minor	5
2339	Tawny Marbled Minor	1 2 5-9
2340	Middle-barred Minor	1-9
2341	Cloaked Minor	2 3 6-9 11
2343	Common Rustic	1-9 11
2345	Small Dotted Buff	1-9 11
2347	Concolorous	1 3-7 9
2349	Mere Wainscot	1-9
2350	Small Wainscot	1-7 9
2352	Dusky Sallow	1 2 5 7-9 11
2353	Flounced Rustic	2 3 5 7 8 9
2360	Ear Moth	3
2364	Frosted Orange	8
2369	Bulrush Wainscot	3 5
2370	Twin-spotted Wainscot	2 8 9
2380	Treble Lines	3 6
2381	Uncertain	1 3 6-9
2382	Rustic	1-9 11
2387	Mottled Rustic	1-10
2389	Pale Mottled Willow	7 8 9
2397	Small Yellow Underwing	3
2410	Marbled White Spot	4 6 7 9
2421	Scarce Silver-lines	1 3 4 6 9
2422	Green Silver-lines	1-9
2423	Oak Nycteoline	1-10
2434	Burnished Brass	1-7 9
2441	Silver Y	1-9 11
2442	Beautiful Golden Y	1-9
2443	Plain Golden Y	1-10
2450	Spectacle	1 2 5 6 8 9
2452	Red Underwing	2-7
2462	Mother Shipton	2-5 7 11
2463	Burnet Companion	3 4 6 11
2466	Blackneck	2 3
2469	Herald	1-9
2489	Fan-foot	1 3 4 5 7 9
2492	Small Fan-foot	1-10

Micro-moths

4	Micropteryx aruncella	2
5	M. calthella	1-4,6 7, K3
6	Eriocrania subpurpurella	1-8, K3
7	E. chrysolepidella	2 (VC 24)
9	E. sparrmannella	2-5
10	E. salopiella	4 7
11	E. cicatricella	7

12	E. sangii	2 4 7
13	E. semipurpurella	2 7
40	Bohemannia pulverosella	3
22	Ectoedemia louisella	2 3
23	E. argyropeza	2 3 4 6 7 9
24	E. turbidella	square Q1
25	E. intimella	3 7
28	E. angulifasciella	1-6, 8 9
29	E. atricollis	1-11
30	E. arcuatella	2
31	E. rubivora	6
34	E. occultella	2 3 6 7
37	E. albifasciella	4 6 8
38	E. subbimaculella	2 3 6 8 9
39	E. heringi	1-10
42	E. septembrella	1-4, 6-9
50	Stigmella aurella	1-10, 12 K3
51	S. fragariella – (syn. of 50)	
58	S. ulmariae	8
63	S. lemniscella	1-3, 5-10, 12
64	S. continuella	3 4
65	S. speciosa	5 10
67	S. plagicolella	1-11
68	S. salicis	1-9, 11
70	S. obliquella	1, P4
73	S. trimaculella	2-6, 10
75	S. floslactella	1-11
77	S. tityrella	1, 3-7, 9 10
79	S. perpygmaeella	4 5 8 9
80	S. ulmivora	1 35-10
81	S. hemargyrella	1 3 5 6 7 9 10
83	S. atricapitella	1 2 5 7-9
84	S. ruficapitella	1-7 9 10
86	S. roborella	1 2 4 5 7 9
89	S. basiguttella	1 4 6-9
92	S. anomalella	1-11
93	S. centifoliella	5 9
95	S. viscerella	1 3 5-8
98	S. catharticella	11
99	S. hybnerella	1-4, 6 8 9 10
100	S. oxyacanthella	2, 4-7, 9-11
107	S. regiella	5 6 7
108	S. crataegella	1 4 5 7 9
111	S. microtheriella	1-9
112	S. luteella	2 4 6 7 10
114	S. glutinosae	4
116	S. lapponica	2 3 4 6 7
117	S. confusella	4 7
121	Pseudopostega crepusculella	6
123	Tischeria ekebladella	3-8
125	Emmetia marginea	3 4, 6-9
127	E. angusticolella	1 4 5 7
128	Phylloporia bistrigella	2 (VC 24)
129	Incurvaria pectinea	2 4
130	I. masculella	2 7 9
131	I. oehlmanniella	6
132	I. praelatella	2
137	Lampronia morosa	7

140	Nematopogon swammerdamella		1 2 6 7 8
141	N. schwarziellus		1
143	N. metaxella		1
148	Nemophora degeerella		2
150	Adela reaumurella		2 3 4 6 7 8
152	A. rufimitrella		2 6
153	A. fibulella		3 7, K3
156	Heliozela resplendella		4
157	H. hammoniella		2
158	Antispila metallella		1-3 6 7 9
159	A. treitschkiella		1 2 7-9
175	Narycia monilifera		3 4 5 6 9
185	Luffia ferchaultella		6 U2
186	Psyche casta		2 3 5 6 7
196	Morophaga choragella		4-
203	Infurcitinea argentimaculella		6
216	Nemapogon cloacella		5
220	N. clematella		2 7 U3
227	Monopis laevigella		8 9, J4
228	M. weaverella		2, 4-9
246	Tinea semifulvella		2, P3
247	T. trinotella		2 4
254	Leucoptera laburnella	Laburnam Leaf Miner	10, P4
260	L. malifoliella	Pear-leaf Blister Moth	4 6 8 10 11
263	Lyonetia clerkella	Apple Leaf Miner	2-8, 10-12
273	Bucculatrix thoracella		10
274	B. ulmella		3 4 6 8 9
275	B. bechsteinella		2-9
282	Caloptilia Elongella		2 4
284	C. rufipennella		2 5 10
286	C. alchimiella		2 5 7
287	C. robustella		2 9
288	C. stigmatella		4 5 7
290	C. semifascia		4 6
293	C. syringella		5 7, P4
297	Eucalybites auroguttella		1-9, 11
301	Parornix betulae		2-5, 7 8
303	P. anglicella		1-12
304	P. devoniella		1-9
305	P. scoticella		3 7 10
308	P. finitimella		1-9, 12
309	Deltaornix torquillella		9
310	Callisto denticulella		1 2 5 6 8 10-12
313	Acrocercops brongniardella		7 9 10
315	Phyllonorycter harrisella		2 3 4, 6-9
317	P. heegeriella		2 3
320	P. quercifoliella		2-9
321	P. messaniella		1 3 4 7 9 10
323	P. oxyacanthae		1-10
324	P. sorbi		10
326	P. blancardella		1, 3-8, 11 12
329	P. spinicolella		1 2 3 5 6 8 9 10
330	P. cerasicolella		6 10
331	P. lantanella		3 4 7 8 9
332	P. corylifoliella		1-11

332a	P. leucographella		10K1
333	P. salictella ssp viminiella		1 4
335	P. salicicolella		1 2 3 7 8 9
337	P. hilarella		1 2 4 6 8 9 11
338	P. cavella		7
341	P. maestingella		1, 3-7, 9 10
342	P. coryli		1-7 9
345	P. rajella		4 10, P4
351	P. lautella		2
352	P. schreberella		1, 3, 5-9
353	P. ulmifoliella		1-9
354	P.Emberizaepennella		10
356	P. tristrigella		1 2 5-10
357	P. stettinensis		4 5,P4
359	P. nicellii		2 3, 5-9
361	P. trifasciella		2 3 7 9
362	P. acerifoliella		1-9, 11
363	P. platanoidella		5
364	P. geniculella		2 7
368	Phyllocnistis unipunctella		4 5 10
385	Anthophila fabriciana		1-4, 6-12
391	Glyphipterix simpliciella	Cocksfoot Moth	2-4 6 7 8 11
401	Argyresthia laevigatella		1
410	A. brockeella		2-5, 9 10
411	A. goedartella		2-6, 9
415	A. retinella		3
416	A. glaucinella		2 3 6 7 9 12
417	A. spinosella		2 3A
421	A. bonnetella		1 2 5 8
422	A. albistria		1 2 5 9 11
424	Yponomeuta evonymella	Bird-cherry Ermine	5 7 9
425	Y. padella	Orchard Ermine	5
427	Y. cagnagella	Spindle Ermine	2 4 5 6 8
430	Y. plumbella		2
436	P'swammerdamia combinella		5 P3
437	Swammerdamia caesiella		4
440	Paraswammerdamia albicapitella		3 6
441	P. lutarea		4, 6-9
443	Cedestis subfasciella		9
447	Roeslerstammia Erxlebella		6 10
449	Prays fraxinella		5
450	Scythropia crataegella	Hawthorn Moth	3
451	Ypsolopha mucronella		1 7
452	Y. nemorella		2 4 7
453	Y. dentella		1 6 7 9
455	Y. scabrella		2 3
457	Y. lucella		1
460	Y. parenthesella		1 2 3 4 6 7
462	Y. sequella		2 6
464	Plutella xylostella	Diamond-back Moth	1-5, 8 9 11
465	P. porrectella		7
469	Eidophasia messingiella		2
470	Orthotelia sparganella		4
481	Epermenia falciformis		1 2 7
490	Coleophora lutipennella		2, 4-9

491	C. gryphipennella		1-5, 7 8 9 12, Q1
492	C. flavipennella		1 2 5 7 8
493	C. serratella		2 3 4 6 7 8
494	C. coracipennella		3 4
495	C. spinella		1-5, 7 9 12
497	C. badiipennella		3 6 7, K3 Q1
499	C. limosipennella		1 5 6 7
501	C. siccifolia		4
504	C. lusciniaepennella		2 3 4 7 12
512	C. binderella		3 6 7 8
513	C. potentillae		2 3
515	C. albitarsella		2 5 6 9 P4
516	C. trifolii		2
518	C. mayrella		2
525	C. solitariella		2 4 7 8 11
526	C. laricella	Larch Case-bearer	2 3 5 7 10 12
533	C. anatipennella	Pistol Case-bearer	1-7, 9
535	C.lbipennella		1-4, 6
536	C. betulella		4
537	C. palliatella		8
553	C. striatipennella		2 3
555	C. follicularis		2
559	C. peribenanderi		1 3 6 7 9 10
581	C. taeniipennella		1 2 3 5 7
582	C. glaucicolella		1 2 3 7
584	C. alticolella		2 6 7 9
587	C. caespititiella		1 2 4 7 8 11
594	Elachista gleichenella		5
602	E. apicipunctella		8
606	E. humilis		2 7
609	E. maculicerusella		7
610	E. argentella		2 3 6 7 11
622	E. adscitella		7
623	E. bisulcella		2 7 9
640	Batia lunaris		2 5 6 9
642	B. unitella		1-10
647	Hoffmannophila pseudospretella	Brown House Moth	7
648	Endrosis sarcitrella	White-shouldered House Moth	3
649	Esperia sulphurella		2 4 6 8 12, K3
658	Carcina quercana		1-9
663	Diurnea fagella		2 4 6 7
664	D. lipsiella		3
666	Semioscopis avellanella		P3
671	Depressaria ultimella		P3
672	D. pastinacella		5, K1
688	Agonopterix heracliana		2 4 7 8 10
689	A. ciliella		4
692	A. subpropinquella		9
695	A.Alstromeriana		2 4, Q1
697	A. arenella		2 4
709	A. liturosa		2 3 5 6 9
713	A. angelicella		5 8
724	Metzneria lappella		2
729	Isophrictis striatella		9
731	Eulamprotes atrella		1 2 4 5 8 9
735	Monochroa tenebrella		3
736	M. lucidella		3

755	Stenolechia gemmella		6
765	Teleiodes vulgella		3
772	Carpatolechia fugitivella		7
774	Teleiodes luculella		2 7
782	Bryotropha senectella		11
787	B. terrella		9
792	Mirificarma mulinella		7
802a	Gelechia sororculella		5
806	G. nigra		6
819	Scrobipalpa costella		2
844	S. larseniella		2 7 8
853	Anacampsis populella		2 6 9
858	Hypatima rhomboidella		3 7
859	Psoricoptera gibbosella		6
866	Brachmia blandella		4 6 8 9
868	Helcystogramma rufescens		2 4 6 8 11
873	Blastobasis lignea		5
874	B. decolorella		2 7 8 9
878	Batrachedra praeangusta		2 9
883	Mompha raschkiella		2 4 5 7 8 11
886	M. ochraceella		3
888	M. propinquella		2 8
892	M subbistrigella		4
893	M.Epilobiella		4
898	Limnaecia phragmitella		3 4
903	Chrysoclista linneella		11
905	Blastodacna hellerella		6
924	Hysterophora maculosana		2 7
925	Phtheochroa. rugosana		2 7
930	Gynnidimorpha alismana		3
936	Cochylimorpha straminea		2
937	Agapeta hamana		1-9, 11
938	A. zoegana		2 5 11
945	Aethes cnicana		1 2 8
946	A. rubigana		2 4 5 7 8
947	A smeathmanniana		2
951	A. beatricella		6 8
962	Cochylis roseana		5 5A 7 8 9 11
965	C. hybridella		2 4
969	Pandemis corylana	Chequered Fruit-tree Tortrix	1 2, 5-9
970	P. cerasana	Barred Fruit-tree Tortrix	1-9
972	P. heparana	Dark Fruit-tree Tortrix	1-5, 8 9 11
977	Archips podana	Large Fruit-tree Tortrix	1 2 3 4 6 8
979	A. crataegana	Brown Oak Tortrix	2 3 4 7 8 9
980	A. xylosteana	Variegated Golden Tortrix	1 3-10
983	Choristoneura hebenstreitella		2 5
986	Syndemis musculana		2, 5-8
987	Ptycholomoides aeriferanus		2 5
989	Aphelia paleana Timothy Tortrix		2 11
993	Clepsis spectrana Cyclamen Tortrix		8 9
994	C. consimilana		8
1000	Ptycholoma lecheana		6 7
1001	Lozotaeniodes formosanus		2 5 6 8 9
1002	Lozotaenia forsterana		3
1010	Ditula angustiorana		1-4 7-10
1011	Pseudargyrotoza conwagana		1-9, 11
1014	Isotrias rectifasciana		2 3 8
1015	Eulia ministrana		2 4 6 7 8

1020	Cnephasia stephensiana	Grey Tortrix	2-5 7 8 9
1021	C. asseclana	Flax Tortrix	1 8
1024	C. incertana	Light-grey Tortrix	2-5 8 9
1025	Tortricodes alternella		3 5A 6 7
1030	Eana incanana		5 8
1032	Aleimma loeflingiana		3
1033	Tortrix viridana	Green Oak Tortrix	1-8
1035	Acleris bergmanniana		2
1036	A. forsskaleana		2-9, 11
1038	A. laterana		1 2, 5-9
1039	A. comariana		2
1042	A. rhombana		1, 4-7, 9
1048	A. variegana	Garden Rose Tortrix	1 2 5 7 9
1050	A. boscana		4
1053	A. hastiana		1 7
1054	A. cristana		9
1062	A.Emargana		1 2 4 6 7 9
1063	Celypha striana		1 4 8 11
1076	C. lacunana		1-4, 6, 8-11
1079	Piniphila bifasciana		2 7 9
1082	Hedya pruniana	Plum Tortrix	1-6, 8
1083	H. nubiferana	Marbled Orchard Tortrix	1-4, 6-9, 11
1084	H. ochroleucana		2 3 4 5 9
1086	H. salicella		2 4 8
1088	Pseudosciaphila branderiana		6
1092	Apotomis turbidana		2 4 6
1093	A. betuletana		1 2, 4-7, 9
1094	A. capreana		1 4 7
1097	Endothenia gentianaeana		1 2 5 5A 8 11 12
1099	E. marginana		11
1108	Lobesia abscisana		2, 4-9
1111	Bactra lancealana		1 3 4 6 7
1113	Eudemis profundana		2 5 7 9
1115	Ancylis achatana		2 3 4 6
1120	A. mitterbacheriana		2 5 7
1122	A. obtusana		2
1126	A. badiana		2 4 5 7
1132	Epinotia subocellana		2 6
1133	E. bilunana		2 4 5
1134	E. ramella		2 4 5 9
1135	E. demarniana		4
1138	E. nisella		1 2 4 9
1139	E. tenerana		9
1142	E. tedella		2 6 7
1150	E. abbreviana		1 2 6 7 8 11
1152	E. maculana		1
1155	E. brunnichana		1 2 4 5 6
1156	E. solandriana		4
1159	Rhopobota naevana		4
1165	Zeiraphera isertana		3, 4-7, 9
1166	Z. grisiana	Larch Tortrix	3 9
1167	Gypsonoma aceriana		6
1169	G. dealbana		1-9
1174	Epiblema cynosbatella		2 3 4 6 7 3a
1175	E. uddmanniana	Bramble Shoot Moth	1-9
1178	E. roborana		2 4 5 7 8 9
1184	E. scutulana		4 8, K1 K3
1184a	E. cirsiana		2 8 U3
1186	E. sticticana		2 11
1197	E. campoliliana		4 6

1200	Eucosma hohenwartiana		6 8 9 11
(1200a	E. fulvana - now listed with 1200)		
1201	E. cana		1-9
1202	E. obumbratana		5 9
1205	Spilonota ocellana	Bud Moth	2, 4-9, 11
1205a	S. laricana		4 5 7 8
1207	Clavigesta purdeyi	Pine Leaf-mining Moth	9
1208	Pseudococcyx posticana		2 8
1210	Rhyacionia buoliana	Pine Shoot Moth	5 6
1211	R. pinicolana		2 6 8 9
1212	R. pinivorana	Spotted Shoot Moth	7 9
1217	Eucosmomorpha albersana		2 4 7
1219	Lathronympha strigana		1 2 6 7 8
1221	Strophedra weirana		3
1222	S. nitidana		4
1227	Pammene inquilina		1
1232	P. populana		2
1236	P. fasciana		2
1243	Cydia pallifrontana		2
1251	C. jungiella		2 4 6 7 U3
1255	C. succedana		7
1257	C. nigricana		11
1260	C. splendana		2, 4-9
1268	C. coniferana		5
1272	Pammene aurana		2 8 K1
1279	Dichrorampha acuminatana		2
1288	Alucita hexadactyla	Twenty-plume Moth	4
1292	Calamotropha paludella		Q1
1293	Chrysoteuchia culmella		1-9, 11 K1
1301	Crambus lathoniellus		1-4, 6-9, 11
1302	C. perlella		2 8
1304	Agriphila straminella		2-12
1305	A. tristella		2-9, 11
1309	A. geniculea		2 7 11 12
1313	Catoptria pinella		2 4 5 8 9
1316	C. falsella		6 8
1329	Donacaula forficella		7
1330	D. mucronella		4
1331	Acentria Ephemerella	Water Veneer	2, 4-9, 11
1332	Scoparia subfusca		2 5 9 11
1333	S. pyralella		3
1334	S. ambigualis		1-8
1334a	S. basistrigalis		9
1338	Dipleurina lacustrata		1-9
1344	Eudonia mercurella		2 4 5 8 9 11
1345	Elophila nymphaeata	Brown China-mark	2 3 4 7
1348	Parapoynx stratiotata	Ringed China-mark	2 3 5 9 11
1350	Nymphula stagnata	Beautiful China-mark	9 11
1356	Evergestis forficalis	Garden Pebble	1 2 4 8
1361	Pyrausta aurata		4 7 9, K3
1362	P. purpuralis		2 4 5
1376	Eurrhypara hortulata		7
1377	Perinephila lancealis		1 2 4 5 6
1378	Phlyctaenia coronata		3 4 8 10
1380	P. perlucidalis		1 3 5 6 8
1385	Ebulea crocealis		1 6
1388	Udea lutealis		7
1390	U. prunalis		1 2 4 5 7 8 9
1392	U. olivalis		1-4, 6-9, 11

1395	U. ferrugalis		2 8 12
1398	Nomophila noctuella	Rush Veneer	1 2, 4-11
1405	Pleuroptya ruralis	Mother of Pearl	1 2, 4-11
1413	Hypsopygia costalis	Gold Triangle	1 2, 4-9, 11
1415	Orthopygia glaucinalis		2 6 8
1424	Endotricha flammealis		5 8 9
1425	Galleria mellonella	Wax Moth	4 6
1426	Achroia grisella	Lesser Wax Moth	7
1428	Aphomia sociella	Bee Moth	7 8 9
1436	Conobathra repandana		2, 4-9
1437	Acrobasis consociella		2 4 5 6 8 9
1439	Trachycera advenella		2 7 9
1452	Phycita roborella		1-9, 11
1454	Dioryctria abietella		5 6 9
1454a	D. schuetzeella		5
1455	D. simpliciella		9
1458	Myelois circumvoluta		2 3 8
1470	Euzophera pinguis		1 2 4 5 7 8 9 11
1481	Homoeosoma sinuella		2 P3
1483	Phycitodes binaevella		5 8
1497	Amblyptilia acanthadactyla		4 5
1498	A. punctidactyla		4
1501	Platyptilia gonodactyla		11
1507	Stenoptilia zophodactylus		7
1509	S. pterodactyla		2 3 4 6 8
1513	Pterophorus pentadactyla		2 4 8
1514	P. galactodactyla		2 4
1517	Adaina microdactyla		1-9
1524	Emmelina monodactyla		1 2 4 6 7 10

Ornithology

Accipiter gentilis	Goshawk	2-5
" nisus	Sparrowhawk	2-8
Acrocephalus schoenobaenus	Sedge Warbler	1
Aegithalos caudatus	Long-tailed Tit	1-11
Aix galericulata	Mandarin Duck	35
Alauda arvensis	Skylark	2-9 11 12
Alcedo atthis	Kingfisher	34 10
Alectoris rufa	Red-legged Partridge	1-12
Anas crecca	Teal	34 10
" penelope	Wigeon	4
" platyrynchos	Mallard	2-6 10 12
Anser anser	Greylag Goose	5 10
Anthus pratensis	Meadow Pipit	5 11 12
" trivialis	Tree Pipit	2
Apus apus	Swift	1-9
Ardea cinerea	Heron	234 10 11 12
Asio otus	Long-eared Owl	3459
Athena noctua	Little Owl	234679 10 12
Aythya fuligula	Tufted Duck	34 10
Branta canadensis	Canada Goose	245 10
Bucephala clangula	Goldeneye	10
Buteo buteo	Buzzard	2-6 9
Caprimulgus europaeus	Nightjar	456
Carduelis cannabina	Linnet	3467
" carduelis	Goldfinch	12378 11 12
" flammea	Redpoll	4
" chloris	Greenfinch	1-12
Certhia familiaris	Tree Creeper	2-9
Columba oenas	Stock Dove	158 11
" palumbus	Woodpigeon	1-12
Corvus corone corone	Crow	1-12
" frugilegus	Rook	1-12
" monedula	Jackdaw	1-12
Cuculus canorus	Cuckoo	1-12
Cygnus olor	Swan	6 10
Delichon urbica	House Martin	10 12
Dendrocopus major	Gt. Spotted Woodpecker	1-11
" minor	Lesser Spotted Woodpecker	123679
Emberiza cirrinella	Yellow Hammer	2-11
" schoeniculus	Reed Bunting	2-68
Erithacus rubecula	Robin	1-12
Falco peregrinus	Peregrine Falcon	4
" subbuteo	Hobby	27
" tinnunculus	Kestrel	1-12
Fringilla coelebs	Chaffinch	1-12
Fulica atra	Coot	234 10 12
Gallingago gallingago	Snipe	4
Gallinula chloropus	Moorhen	1-12
Garrulus glandarius	Jay	1-12
Hirundo rustica	Swallow	23468 10 12
Larus argentatus	Gull Herring	46 11
" marinus	" Gt. Black-backed	2 11

"　minutus	"　Little	2
"　ridibundus	"　Blackheaded	268
Locustella naevia	Grasshopper Warbler	1-7
Loxia curvivostra	Crossbill	247
Luscinia megarhynchos	Nightingale	124679
Milvus milvus	Red Kite	38
Motacilla alba yarrellii	Pied Wagtail	2-10
"　　cinerea	Grey　"	10
Numenius arquata	Curlew	2
Oenanthe oenanthe	Wheatear	2
Pandion haliaetus	Osprey	1-12
Parus ater	Coal Tit	2-10
"　caeruleus	Blue Tit	1-12
"　major	Great Tit	1-12
"　montanus	Willow Tit	15
"　palustris	Marsh Tit	1-79
Passer domesticus	Sparrow	2368 10 12
"　montanus	Tree Sparrow	456 11
Pavo cristatus	Peafowl	346
Perdix perdix	English Partridge	34789
Phasianus colchicus	Pheasant	1-12
Phoenicurus phoenicurus	Redstart	24
Phylloscopus sibilatrix	Wood Warbler	24
"　　trochilus	Willow Warbler	1-9 12
"　　collybita	Chiff Chaff	1-9 12
Pica pica	Magpie	1-12
Picus viridus	Green Woodpecker	1-12
Pluvialis apricaria	Golden Plover	23
Prunella modularis	Dunnock	1-12
Pyrrhula pyrrhula	Bullfinch	2-12
Rallus aquaticus	Water Rail	5
Regulus regulus	Goldcrest	1-9
Saxicola torquata	Stonechat	5
Scolopax rusticola	Woodcock	1-9
Sitta europaea	Nuthatch	234678 10
Sterna hirundo	Tern	4
Streptopelia decaocto	Collared Dove	1-12
"　　turtur	Turtle Dove	1-79
Strix aluco	Tawny Owl	1-10 12
Sturnus vulgaris	Starling	2-10
Sylvia atricapilla	Blackcap	1-9 12
"　borin	Garden Warbler	1-10
"　communis	Whitethroat	1-8
"　curruca	Lesser Whitethroat	14
Tachybaptus ruficollis	Little Grebe	34 10
Tringa ochropus	Green Sandpiper	2
Troglodytes troglodytes	Wren	1-12
Turdus iliacus	Redwing	1-9
"　merula	Blackbird	1-12
"　philomelus	Song Thrush	1-9
"　pilaris	Fieldfare	1-12
"　viscivorus	Mistle Thrush	1-10
Tyto alba	Barn Owl	34 10
Vanellus vanellus	Lapwing	23467 11 12

Mammals

Apodemus sylvaticus	Wood/Field Mouse	1-12
Capreolus capreolus	Roe Deer	35
Cervus dama	Fallow Deer	1-10 12
" elaphus	Red Deer	234
Clethrionomys glareolus	Bank Vole	2346
Erinaceus europaeus	Hedgehog	2-6 10
Hydropotes inermis	Chinese Water Deer	35
Lepus europeaeus	Hare	1-12
Meles meles	Badger	1-7 12
Micromys minutus	Harvest Mouse	2
Microtus agrestis	Field Vole	234
Muntiacus reevesi	Muntjac Deer	1-12
Mustela erminea	Stoat	1-12
" nivalis	Weasel	1-12
" vison	Mink	23478
Myotis daubentoni	Daubentons Bat	10
" nattereri	Natterers Bat	10
Nyctalus noctula	Noctule Bat	10
Oryctolagus cuniculus	Rabbit	1-12
Pipistrellus pipistrellus	Pipistrelle Bat	2-5 10
Plecotus auritus	Long-eared Bat	2-5 10
Rattus norvegicus	Brown Rat	1-12
Sciurus carolinensis	Grey Squirrel	1-12
Sorex araneus	Com. Shrew	234 10 12
" minutus	Pygmy Shrew	234
Vulpes vulpes	Fox	1-12

Reptiles and Amphibians

Anguis fragilis	Slow-worm	23467 10
Bufo bufo	Toad	234 10 11 12
Natrix natrix	Grass Snake	1-12
Rana temporaria	Frog	2349 10 12
Triturus cristatus	Great Crested Newt	34 10
" helveticus	Palmate Newt	23
" vulgaris	Smooth Newt	23467 10 11

Mollusca

Arion ater	Black Slug	1-6
" circumscriptus	Slug	246
" rugus	Red Slug	146
" subfuscus	Dusky Slug	3
Anodonta cygnea	Swan Mussel	10
Cochlicopa lumbricella	Snail	46

Disus rotundatus	Rounded Snail	346
Helix aspersa	Garden Snail	1-12
" hortensis	White-lipped Snail	14 10
" nemoralis	Dark-lipped Snail	1-6 10
Hyalinia alliaria	Garlic Glass Snail	3
" cellaria	Cellar Snail	46
" nitidula	Smooth Glass Snail	46
Limax marginatus	Tree Slug	46
" maximus	Great Grey Slug	46
Limnaea peregra	Wandering Pond Snail	346 10
" stagnalis	Great Pond Snail	34 10
" truncatula	Dwarf Pond Snail	346
Monacha cantiona	Kentish Snail	46
Pisidium milium	Pea Mussel	34 10
Planorbis nautileus	Nautilus Ramshorn Snail	3
Potamopyrgus jenkinsi	Jenkins Spire Shell Snail	34
Theodoxus fluviatilis	Nerite Snail	10
Trichia lispida	Hairy Snail	46

Odonata

Aeshna cyanea	Southern Hawker	1-12
" grandis	Brown Hawker	34
" juncea	Common Hawker	34
" mixta	Migrant Hawker	1-12
Anax imperator	Emperor	34 10
Brachytron pratense	Hairy Hawker	4
Calopteryx splendens	Banded Demoiselle	34
" virgo	Beautiful Demoiselle	345
Coenagrion puella	Azure Damselfly	4 10
Cordulia aenea	Downy Emerald	4
Enallagma cyathigerum	Common Blue Damselfly	1-12
Ischnura elegans	Blue-tailed Damselfly	234 10
Lestes sponsa	Emerald Damselfly	3
Libellula depressa	Broad-bodied Chaser	234 10
" quadrimaculata	Four-spotted Chaser	234 10
Orthetrum cancellatum	Black-tailed Skimmer	4 10
Platycnemis pennipes	White-legged Damselfly	4
Pyrrhosoma nymphula	Large Red Damselfly	2347 10
Sympetrum sanguineum	Ruddy Darter	23479 10 12
" striolatum	Common Darter	2-578 10 12

Orthoptera

Chorthippus brunneus	Com. Field Grasshopper	12368-12
" parallelus	Meadow Grasshopper	1-8 10
Leptophyes punctatissima	Speckled Bush-cricket	23467
Meconema thalassinum	Oak Bush-cricket	2-8 10
Omocestus viridulus	Com. Green Grasshopper	23467 10
Pholidoptera griseoaptera	Dark Bush-cricket	1-12
Tetrix subulata	Slender Groundhopper	234
" undulata	Com. Groundhopper	134 11

Hemiptera

Acanthosoma haemorrhoidale	Hawthorn Shield Bug	1-12
Anthocoris nemoralis nemoralis	Flower Bug	3
" nemorum	" "	13
Aphrodes difusciatus	Leafhopper	1
Aphrophora alni	Froghopper	369 10 12
" salicis	"	4
Atractotomus mali	Plant Bug	3
Berytinus minor	Stilt Bug	34
Callicorixa praeusta	Water Boatman	4
Calocoris stysi	Nettle Bug	6
" norvegicus	Plant Bug	3
Campyloneura virgula	" "	3
Capsus ater	Mirid Bug	23478 10 11
Centrotus cornutus	Horned Tree-hopper	2346-10
Cercopis vulnerata	Froghopper	1-12
Cicadella viridis	Green Leaf-hopper	1-8 12
Corixa dentipes	Water Boatman	4
" falleni	" "	4 10
" punctata	" "	2346 11 12
Cymatia bonsdorffi	" "	4
Deraeocoris ruber	Plant Bug	3
Dicyphus errans	Capsid Bug	5
Dolichonabis limbatus	Marsh Damsel Bug	135 11 12
Dolycoris baccarum	Sloe Bug	2-69 11 12
Elasmostethus interstinctus	Birch Shield Bug	1-8 10
Elasmucha grisea	Parent Bug	1-10 12
Elymana sulphurella	Leafhopper	3
Empicoris vagabundus	Assasin Bug	5

Evacanthus interruptus	Froghopper	46
Eysacoris fabricii	Shield Bug	245
Gastrodes abietum	Spruce Cone Bug	5
Gerris lacustris	Pondskater	2347 10-12
Hebrus ruficeps	Sphagnum Bug	3
Hesperocorixa linnei	Water Boatman	4
" sahlbergi	" "	4
Heterotoma merioptera	Capsid Bug	3
" planicornis	Plant Bug	3
Himacerus apterus	Tree Damsel Bug	2357 12
Hydrometra stagnorum	Water Measurer	2346 10-12
Iassus lanio	Leafhopper	3-12
Ilyocoris cimicoides	Saucer Bug	4
Kalmanius flavomarginatus	Damsel Bug	3
Ledra aurita	Leafhopper	2
Leptoterna dolabrata	Grass Bug	2369 11
" ferrugata	" "	3
Liocoris tripustulatus	Nettle Bug	3
Loricula elegantula	Dwarf Bug	3
Lygocoris contaminatus	Plant Bug	3
" lucorum	" "	3
" pabulinus	Green Capsid Bug	1-12
" spinolai	Plant Bug	3
Lygus rugulipennis	Leafhopper	2
Macrosteles variatus	"	8
Megaloceraea recticornis	Grass Bug	3
Melachocoris chlorizans	Plant Bug	3
Miris striatus	Mirid Bug	1-12
Nabis ferus	Field Damsel Bug	2
" rugosus	Damsel Bug	239 11
Nabricula limbatus	Damsel Bug	3
Neophilaenus lineatus	Froghopper	11
Nepa cinerea	Water Scorpion	34
Notonecta glauca	Backswimmer	346 10 11
" viridis	"	34 10 12
Notostira elongata	Mirid Bug	23467
Oncotylus viridiflavus	Plant Bug	3
Orthanotus rutifrous	" "	3
Orthops campestris	" "	3
Orthotylus marginalis	" "	3
" prasinus	" "	3
Palomena prasina	Green Shield Bug	237
Pentatoma rufipes	Forest Bug	2-579 12
Philaenus spumaris	Froghopper	1-12
Phytocoris longipennis	Plant Bug	3
" populi	" "	3
" tiliae	" "	3
Phylus coryli	" "	3
" melanocephalus	Capsid Bug	5
Picromerus bidens	Shield Bug	13569 10
Piezodorus lituratus	Gorse Shield Bug	3
Pinslitus cervinus	Plant Bug	3
Pithanus maekelii	Assasin Bug	356 12
Plagiognathus arbustorum	Plant Bug	3
" chrysanthemi	" "	3
Plesiocoris rugicollis	Apple Bug	1
Ploiaria domestica	Assasin Bug	1
Polymerus unifasciatus	Mirid Bug	12
Psallus varians	Capsid Bug	36
Ranatra linearis	Water Scorpion	3
Sehirus bicolor	Pied Shield Bug	236 10 12

Sigara distincta	Water Boatman	4
" falleni	" "	4
" fossarum	" "	4
" lateralis	" "	4
Stenodema calcaratum	Plant Bug	234
" laevigatum	Grass Bug	2369 11
Thamnotettix confinis	Leafhopper	13
Tingis ampliata	Lace Bug	3
" cardui	" "	3
Trigonotylus ruficornis	Grass Bug	3
Troilus luridus	Shield Bug	2
Velia caprai	Water Cricket	2346
" currens	" "	1-4 10-12

Diptera

Achalcus flavicollis	Dolichopodid fly	3
Aeds cinereus	Mosquito	4
Amauromyza labiatarum	Miner fly	4
Anasimyia contracta	Hover fly	34
" lineata	" "	3
Argyra argeatina	Dolichopodid fly	3
" leucocephala	"	3
" vestita	"	3
Asilus crabroniformis	Robber fly	3
" ocellata	" "	2
Asteia concinna		3
Atherix ibis	Snipe fly	3
Authromyza bifasciata		3
" gracilis		3
" pallida		3
Autrolimnophila ochracea	Conopid fly	4
Baccha elongata	Hover fly	6
Beris chalybata	Soldier fly	4
" vallata	" "	3
Bibio hortulanus	Bibionid fly	47
" marci	St Marks fly	1-12
Bicellaria vana	Empid fly	3
Bombylius major	Bee fly	1-12
Campsicnemus curvipes	Dolichopodid fly	3
" scambus		3
Cephalops guermanicus	Pipunculid fly	4
Cetema neglecta	Grass fly	3
" similis	" "	3
Chaetorellia jaceae	Picture-wing fly	3
Chamaemyia aridella	"	3
" fasciata	"	34
Chaoborus crystallinus	Gnat	346 12
Cheilosia albipila	Hover fly	4
" illustrata	"	4
" grossa	"	4
" pagana	"	4
Chironomus plumosa	Midge	2346 12
Chloromyia formosa	Soldier fly	3
Chlorops gracilis	Pipunculid fly	34
" scalaris	Grass fly	3
" speciosa	"	3
Chrysopilus asiliformis	Snipe fly	3
" cristatus	"	34
Chrysops caecutiens	Horse fly	3

" relictus	"	2346 11 12
Chrysotus cilipes	Dolichopodid fly	3
" graminicus	"	3
Colobaea distincta	Snail-killing fly	4
Conops quadrifasciata	Thickheaded fly	46
Cordilura albipes	Dung fly	3
" pubera	"	3
" pudica	"	3
Chriorhina asilica	Hover fly	4
Crorrhina ranunculi	"	34
Cryptonerva tarsata	Grass fly	3
Ctenophora bimaculata	Cranefly	3
Culex pipiens	Mosquito	3
Darylomorpha hungarica	Pipunculid fly	4
Dasineura urticae	Nettle Gall fly	479
Dicraeus vagans	Grass fly	3
Dinocras cephalotes	Stone fly	234
Dixa sp.	Midge	34
Delichopus brevipennis	Dolichopodid fly	34
" festivus	"	3
" griseipennis	"	3
" plumipes	"	3
" trivialis	"	3
" ungulatus	"	3
" wahlbergi	"	3
Drosophila picta	Fruit fly	3
Elachiptera cornuta	Grass fly	3
Elgiva cueuldria	Snail-killing fly	34
Empis aestiva	Empid fly	3
" albipennis	"	3
" livida	"	3
" praevia	"	3
" stercorea	"	348 10
" tessellata	"	23468 11 12
Eoseristalis arbustorum	Hover fly	467 11
Epiphragma ocellaris	Cranefly	4
Episyrphus balteatus	Hover fly	46 11 12
Erioptera griseiventris	Cranefly	4
" stictica	"	4
Eriothrix rufomaculatus	Parasite fly	2
Eristalis arbustorum	Hover fly	3
" nemorum	"	4
" pertinax	"	34
" tennax	"	34679 10
Euribia cardui	Thistle Gall fly	2-7 10-12
Geomyza combinata	Shoot fly	3
Gymnochaeta viridis	Tachnid fly	8
Haematopota pluvialis	Cleg	1-12
Hermandia globuli	Aspen Pea Gall fly	36
Helius flavus	Cranefly	4
" longirostis	"	4
Helophilus pendulus	Hover fly	3467
Hercostomus parvilamellatus	Dolichopodid fly	4
" silvestris	"	3
Herina germinationis	Picture-wing fly	3
" lugubris	"	3
Hybos femoratus	Empid fly	3
Hydromia dorsalis	Snail-killing fly	3
Hypophillus obscurellus	Dolichopodid fly	3
Ilione abbiseta	Snail-killing fly	4
Lamprochromus strobli	Dolichopodid fly	3

Laphria marginata	Robber fly	4
Leptogaster cylindrica	"	3
Leucozona laterauria	Hover fly	4
"　　lucorum	"	3479
Limnia paludicola	Snail-killing fly	34
"　unguicornis	"	3
Limnophila ferruginea	Cranefly	4
"　　nemoralis	"	4
Limonia dumetorum	"	4
"　flavipes	"	4
"　mitis f-lutea	"	4
"　nubeculosa	"	468 10 12
"　tripunctata	"	4
Lonchoptera furcata	Pointed-wing fly	3
"　lutea	"	3
Loxocera ichneumonea	Pictur Wing fly	3
Lucilia caesar	Greenbottle	38
Lyciella decipiens	Picture Wing fly	3
Machimus atricapillus	Robber fly	3
Medetera petrophila	Diolichopodid fly	3
"　truncorum	"	3
Melanostoma mellinum	Hover fly	3479
"　　scalare	"	34
Meliscaeva auricollis	"	4
Melophilus appendiculatus	Cranefly	4
"　obscurus	"	4
Meredon equestris	Narcissus fly	13467 10
Meromyza femorata	Grass fly	3
"　　sorocula	"	3
"　　triangulara	"	3
"　　variegata	"	3
Metasyrphus luniger	Hover fly	7
Micromorphus albipes	Dolichopodid fly	3
Microphorus crassipes	Empid fly	3
Minettia rivosa ·	Picture-wing fly	3
Myatropa florea	Hover fly	134678
Nemotelus nigrinus	Soldier fly	4
Neoascia meticulosa	Hover fly	4
"　tenur	"	34
Nephrotoma appendiculata	Cranefly	4
"　　flavipalpis	"	4
"　maculata	"	4
"　quadrifarea	"	4
Neurigona pallida	Dolichopodid fly	4
Ocydromia glabricula	Empid fly	3
Odontomyia viridula	Soldier fly	3
Opomyza florum	Shoot fly	3
"　　germinationis	"	3
"　petrei	"	3
Ormosia nodulosa	Cranefly	4
Otites guttata		4
Oxycera morrisii	Soldier fly	3
"　trilineata	"	3
Pachygaster atra	"	3
Paracrocera orbiculies	Top-horned Hunchback fly	3
Paragus haemorrhous	Hover fly	3
Parhelophilus frutetorum	"	4
Parydra coarctata	Shore fly	3
"　fossarum	"	3
"　quadripunctata	"	3
Pelidnoptera fuscipennis	Snail-killing fly	4

Pericoma fuliginosa	Midge	4
Perla bipunctata	Stone fly	3
Pherbellia albocostata	Snail-killing fly	4
" dubia	"	4
" ventralis	"	234
Phyllodromia melanocephalus	Empid fly	3
Platycheirus albimanus	Hover fly	4
" cyaneus	"	3
" clypeatus	"	3 11
" europaeus	"	4
" scambus	"	4
" scutulatus	"	4
" tarsalis	"	4
Platypalpus coarctatus	Empid fly	3
" cothurnatus	"	3
" kirtlingensis	"	3
" longisetus	"	3
" minutus	"	3
" pallidicornis	"	3
" ruficornis	"	3
Poecilobothrus nobilitatus	Dolichopodid fly	3
Psacadina verbekei	Snail-killing fly	4
Pseudolimnophila lucorum	Cranefly	4
Ptychoptera contaminata	"	34
Pyrophaena rosarum	Hover fly	34
Raphium appendiculatum	Dolichopodid fly	3
Renocera pallida	Snail-killing fly	34
Rhagio scolopacea	Snipe fly	34
Rhopalopterum femoralis	Grass fly	3
Sarophaga frenata		4
Scaeva pyrastri	Hover fly	2
" selenitica	"	4
Scatella tennicosta	Shore fly	3
Scaptomyza pallida	Fruit fly	3
Scathophaga furcata		3
" stercoraria		2347 10
Sciapus longulus	Dolichopodid fly	3
" platyperus	"	3
Sepedon sphegea	Snail-killing fly	3
Sepsis cynipsea	Lesser Dung fly	3
" flavimana	" "	3
" orthocnemis	"	3
Sphaerophoria bankowskae	Hover fly	4
" scripta	"	7 11
Sphegina clunipes	"	4
Suillia variegata		8
Sympycnus aenicoxa	Dolichopodid fly	3
" desoutteri	"	3
Syntormon denticulatus	"	3
Syritta pipiens	Hover fly	11
Syrphus balteatus	"	2356
" pyrstri	"	3
" ribesii	"	1-12
" torvus	"	4
Tabanus sudeticus	Horse fly	34 ,10
Tachina fera	Tachnid fly	3
Tachydromia aemula	Empid fly	3
Tanyptera atrata	Cranefly	5
Tenchophorus monocanthus	Dolichopodid fly	3
" signatus	"	3
" spinigerellus	"	3

Tephrites bardanae	Picture-wing fly	34
" vespertina	"	3
	"	3
Terellia ruficauda	Snail-killing fly	3
Thrypticus bellus	Dolichopodid fly	3
" nigricauda	"	3
Tipula luna	Cranefly	5
" lunata	"	4
" maxima	"	4
" oleracea	"	1-6 12
" paludosa	"	6 11
Trichocera hiemalis	Winter Gnat	4
Tricholauxania praeusta	Picture-wing fly	4
Trichopsomyia flavitarsis	Hover fly	4
Trypetoptera punctulata	Snail-killing fly	4
Urophora cardui	Picture-wing fly	3
" jaceana	"	3
" stylata	"	3
Volucella bombylans	Hover fly	2-12
" inanis	"	23467 10 12
" pellucens	"	1-12
Xylota segnis	"	4
" sylvarum	"	146
Xyphosia miliaria	Picture-wing fly	3

Hymenoptera

Allantus cinctus	Sawfly	24
Amblyteles armatorious	Ichneumon	6
Andrena albicans	Solitary Bee	4 10 12
" haemorrhoa	" "	2
Andricus fecundator	Hop Gall – Oak	238
" kollari	Marble Gall – Oak	1-12
" quercuscalicis	Knopper Gall – Oak	1-10 12
Apis mellifera	Honey Bee	2-79 10 12
Arge ustulata	Sawfly	12
Biorhiza pallida	Oak Apple Gall	2-79 10 12
Bombus hortorum	Bumble Bee	14 11
" lapidarius	" "	1-79-12
" lucorum	" "	34 11
" muscorum	" "	246 10
" pascuorum	" "	4
" pratorum	" "	479 11
" terrestris	" "	2-12
Cephus pygmaeus	Wheat-stem Borer Sawfly	34
Chrysis ignita	Sawfly	3
Cladius viminalis	" Poplar	4
Croesus septentrionalis	"	234
Cynips divisa	Pea Gall - Oak	257
" quercusfolii	Cherry Gall - Oak	1-468 10 11
Diplolepis eleganteriae	Pea Gall - Rose	346 10
" mayri	Rose Gall	23468
" nervosus	Spiked Pea Gall - Rose	1-46 11 12
" rosae	Bedeguar Gall - Rose	1-12
Dolichovespula norvegica	Wasp Norwegian	347 11
Ichneumon suspiciosus	Ichneumon	234
Liposthenus latreillei	Gall Ground Ivy	1-8 11
Lophyrus pini	Sawfly Pine	6
Megachile centuncularis	Leaf-cutter Bee	12478 10
Mellinus arvensis	Digger Wasp	8

Netelia testacea	Ichneumon	3
Neuroterus albipes	Smooth Spangle Gall - Oak	1-12
Neuroterus numismalis	Silk Button Gall - Oak	1-12
Neuroterus quercusbaccarum	Spangle Gall - Oak	1-12
Nomada marshamella	Cuckoo Bee	3
Ophion luteus	Ichneumon	234
Pimpla instigator	"	46
Pontania proxima	Sawfly	12
Psithyrus sylvestris	Cuckoo Bee	4
" vestalis	" "	4
Rhogogaster viridis	Sawfly	346 12
Sirex juvencus	"	346 12
Tenthredo arcuata	"	3
Urocerus gigas	Horntail	2-57
Vespa crabro	Hornet	2-10 12
Vespula germanica	Wasp German	1-4 10
Vespula rufa	" Red	25 11
Vespula vulgaris	" Common	1-12

Coleoptera

Acilius sulcatus	water beetle	234 10 11
Acupalpus meridianus	ground beetle	3
Adalia 2-punctata	Ladybird 2 spot	1-12
" 10-punctata	" 10 spot	1-10
Agabus bipustulatus	water beetle	234
Agapanthia villosviridescens	Longhorn beetle	249 10 12
Agonum assimile	ground beetle	3
Agriotes lineatus	Click beetle	367
Alosterna tabacicolor	Longhorn beetle	37
Amara aenea	ground beetle	3
Amphimallon solstitiale	Summer Chafer	3
Anaglyptus mysticus	Longhorn beetle	2789
Anatis ocellata	Eyed Ladybird	1-10
Anaspis maculata	Tumbling Flower beetle	3
" thoracia	" " "	3
Anisotoma humeralis	Round Fungus beetle	3
Aphodius fimetarius	Dung beetle	2346 10
" rufus	" "	134578
Apoderus coryli	Weevil	6 12
Apthona euphorbiae		2
Aridius nodifer	Mould beetle	3
Athous bicolor	Click beetle	3
" haemorroidalis	" "	1-12
Bembidion punctulatum	ground beetle	4 10
Calvia 14-guttata	Cream-spot Ladybird	1-7 10 11 12
Cantharis fusca	Sailor beetle	456 10 12
" livida	Soldier beetle	11
" pellucida	Wood Sailor beetle	3
" rustica	Soldier beetle	1-12
Carabus auratus	ground beetle	12
" violaceus	Violet ground beetle	2367 11 12
Cassida rubiginosa	Tortoise beetle	2-5 10
" viridis	" "	6
Chalcoides fulvicornis	Leaf beetle	3
Chilocorus renipustulatus	Kidneyspot Ladybird	124679 11
Chrysolina polita	Leaf beetle	1-7
" populi	" "	47

Scientific name	Common name	Numbers
Chrysomela vigintipinctata	" "	4
Cicindela campestris	Green Tiger beetle	3
Cionus alauda	Weevil	4
" hortulanus	" "	4
" scrophulariae	" "	24
Cis alni	Small Fungus beetle	3
Clytus arietis	Wasp beetle	1-12
Coccinella 7-punctata	Ladybird 7 spot	1-12
Colymbetes fuscus	water beetle	2
Crepidodera transversa	Leaf beetle	3
Cryptocephalus coryli	" "	3
Curculio nucum	Nut Weevil	1-12
Dacne bipustulata	Shiny Fungus beetle	3
Dalopius marginatus	Click beetle	256
Dorcus paraellelipipedus	Lesser Stag beetle	1-478 12
Dascillus cervinus		3
Denticollis linearis	Click beetle	3
Deronectes depressus	water beetle	234
Dytiscus marginalis	Great Diving beetle	347 10
Endomychus coccineus	Fungus beetle	
Exochonus quadripustulatus	Pine Ladybird	1367
Feronia nigrita	ground beetle	56
Geotrupes stercorarius	Dor beetle	2678
Glischrochilus hortensis	Sap beetle	7
Gnathoncus nannetensis	Carrion beetle	3
Gyrinus natator	Whirligig beetle	234 10 11
Gyrohypnus punctulatus	Rove beetle	3
Halipus fulvus	water beetle	234
Halyzia 16-guttata	Orange Ladybird	34 10
Harmonia 4-punctata	Cream-streaked Ladybird	58
Harpalus affinis	ground beetle	24578
Hydrobius fuscipes	water beetle	34 11
Hygrobia tarda	Screech beetle	234
Hylesinus crenatus	Ambrosia beetle	3
Hyphrydus ovatus	water beetle	234 11
Ilybius ater	" "	11
" fuliginosus	" "	4 10 11
Laccobius alutaceus	" "	34
" minutus	" "	34 10 11
Laccophilus minutus	" "	4
Lagria hirta		9
Lampyris noctiluca	Glow-worm	2-6
Leiopus nebulosus	Longhorn beetle	46
Lophloeus tessulatus	Weevil	3
Malachius bipustulatus	Red-tipped Flower beetle	1-12
Majthinus flaveolus	Soldier beetle	137
Melebotus villosus	Click beetle	3
Meligethes aeneus	Pollen beetle	1-12
Melolontha melolontha	Cockchafer	24568 10 11
Microcara testacea		3
Micraspis 16-punctata	Ladybird 16 spot	34579 12
Mordella villosa	Tumbling Flower beetle	2
Mycetochara humeralis	Darkling beetle	3
Mycetophagus multipunctatus	Hairy Fungus beetle	3
" piceus	" " "	3
" quadripustulatus	" " "	3
Myrrha 18-guttata	Ladybird 18 spot	6
Myzia oblongoguttata	Striped Ladybird	9
Nicrophorus humator	Burying beetle	3
" vespilloides	" "	3468 10 11 12
Noterus capricornis	water beetle	234

Notiophilus bigattatus	Sun beetle	3
Oedermera lurida	Thick-legged Flower beetle	3
Oedermera nobilis	Flower beetle	1–7 10
Ocypus globulifer	Rove beetle	34
" olens	Devils Coach-horse	1-12
Oncomera femorata		7
Othius punctulatus	Rove beetle	347
Otiorhynchus singularis	Weevil	2
Oxypoda alternans	Fungus beetle	2347
Phaedon tumidulus	Celery-leaf beetle	3
Philonthus addendus	Rove beetle	3
" cephalotes	" "	3
Phloephagus lignarius	Weevil	3
Phyllobius argentatus	"	14679 10 12
" pomaceus	"	257 12
" sericerus	"	12
Phyllotreta nemorum	Flea beetle	2
" undulata	" "	11
Platambus maculatus	water beetle	234 10 11
Platycis minutus	Net-winged beetle	7
Pocadius ferrugineus	Sap beetle	2
Progonocherus hispidus	Longhorn beetle	8 12
Propylea 14-punctata	Ladybird 14 spot	23-79-11
Pseudotriphyllus suturalis	Hairy Fungus beetle	3
Psyllobora 22-punctata	Ladybird 22 spot	246-11
Pterostichus madida	ground beetle	3
" niger	" "	3 12
Pyrochroa coccinea	Cardinal beetle	3
" serraticornis	" "	1-12
Quedius cruenatus	Rove beetle	3
" nitipennis	" "	4
Rhagium bifasciatum	Two-banded Longhorn	347
" mordax	Longhorn beetle	2-10
Rhagonycha fulva	Hogweed Bonking beetle	3789 11
Rhynchites aequatus	Weevil	6
Saperda populnea	Small Poplar Longhorn	235
Scaphidium quadrimaculatum	Shiny Fungus beetle	26
Scirtes hemisphaericus	Marsh beetle	3
Scolytus intricatus	Ambrosia beetle	35
Serica brunnea	Cockchafer	3 11
Silpha atrata	Carrion beetle	34678 10 12
" carinata	Black Carrion beetle	5
Sinodendron cylindricum	Rhinocerus beetle	345
Stenocorus meridianus	Longhorn beetle	1-10
Strangalia maculata	Spotted Longhorn	1-12
Tachyporus hypnorum	Rove beetle	3
Thanasimus formicarius	Ant beetle	3 11
Thea 22-punctata	Ladybird 22 spot	1-11
Timarcha tenebricosa	Bloody-nosed beetle	34
Triplax russica	Shiny Fungus beetle	3

Plecoptera

Dinocras cephalotes	Stonefly	3
Perla bipunctata	"	23

Dermaptera

Forficula auricularia	Earwig	1-12
Labia minor	Lesser Earwig	4

Mecoptera

Panorpa communis	Scorpion fly	2-8 10 11 12

Neuroptera

Chrysopa perla	Lacewing	3
" septempunctata	"	1-12
Hemerobius humuli	Hop Lacewing	4 12
Raphidia notata	Snakefly	23 12
Sialis lutaria	Alder fly	1-6 10 11 12
Sisyra fuscata	Lacewing	247 10

Trichoptera

Arthripsodes aterrimus	Caddis fly	3
Glyphotaelius pellucidus	"	4
Limnophilus flavicornis	"	34
" lunatus	"	3
" rhombicus	"	4
Mystacides azurea	"	3
Phryganea grandis	"	3
Triaenodes bicolor	"	3

Centipedes and Millipedes

Cylindroiulus sylvarum	1-7 10
Cryptops hortensis	1
Haplophilus subterraneus	236
Lithobius forficatus	34578 12
" variegatus	236
Necrophloeophagus longicornis	8
Polydesmus colplanatus	2467 10 12
" angustus	3
Scutigerella immaculata	2
Tachypodoilus niger	2358

Woodlice

Armadillidium vulgare	8
Glomeris marginata	2
Oniscus asellus	123678
Philoscia muscorum	1
Porcellio scaber	2
Trichoniscus pusillus	4

Harvestmen

Leiobunum rotundum	2-8 10 12
Nemastoma bimaculatum	468
Phalangium opilio	1-4

Arachnida

Achaeranea lunata	14
Agelena labyrinthica	1
Agroeca brunnea	9
Alopecosa pulverulenta	11
Amanrobius fenestralis	345
" similis	349 10
Anelosimus vittatus	34
Anyphaena accentuata	14-79
Araneus cucurbitinus	2467
" diadenatus	24679 10 12
" marmoreus	6
" " v. pyramidatus	1345
" quadratus	124
" sturmi	10
Araniella curcurbitina	12
Arctosa perita	11
Bathyphantes gracilis	146 10
" nigricus	47
Centromerita bicolor	56
" concinna	1
Centromerus sylvatica	9
Cheiracanthium erraticum	15
Chocorua picina	4
Clubonia comata	179
" corticalis	11
" lutescens	146 11
" phragmitis	4
" reclusa	6
" terrestris	1
Cyclosa conica	67
Diaea dorsata	57 10
Dictyna arundinacea	146 11
" uncinata	11
Dicymbium nigrum	6
" tibiale	1
Diplocephalus latifrons	4
Diplostyla concolor	13469 10 11
Dismodicus bifrons	16
Drapetisea socialis	9
Drassodes cupreus	4
" lapidosus	1
Dysdera crocata	11
Elopnogantha ovata	67
Entelecara erythropus	469
Episinus angulatus	25
Erigone atra	67
" dentipalpis	67
Ero cambridgei	156 10
" furcata	69
Euophrys frontalis	11
Floronia bucculenta	167

Gibbarenea gibbosa	1
Gonatium rubellum	9
" rubens	1459
Hahnia montana	234
Harpactea hombergi	4
Helophora insignis	3
Hypsosinga pygmaea	3
Kaestneria dorsalis	4
" pullata	1
Labulla thoracica	14 10
Larinioides cornutus	4 11
Lepthyphantes alacris	3579
" cristatus	1356
" ericaeus	4
" flavipes	3567
" mengei	6
" minutus	9
" obscurus	1
" pallidus	3 11
" tenuis	13-79-11
" zimmermanni	13-79 10
Linyphia hortensis	6
" triangularis	147
Lycosa amentata	469 10 12
Macrargus rufus	37
Maso sundevalli	1
Meioneta rurestris	5
Meta merianne	11
" segmentata	2346
Metellina mengei	14-79 10
" segmentata	134
Micaria pulicaria	11
Micrargus apertus	15
" herbigradus	69
Micrommata virescens	234
Microneta viaria	13569 10
Misumena calycina	234
" vatia	1247 10 12
Neon reticulatus	6
Neottiura bemaculata	1
Neriene clathrata	13569
" montana	14-7
" peltata	47
Nuctena cornuta	4
" umbratica	1-46
Oedothorax apicatus	11
" retusus	16
Ostearius melanopyginus	11
Ozyptila praticola	12 10
" trux	4
Pachignatha clerki	16
" degeeri	1579
" listeri	14
Pardosa amentata	1467 11
" lugubris	6
" palustris	16 11
" prativaga	146 11
" pullata	467
" saltans	1
Philodromus aureolis	25
" cespitum	11

Pholcomma gibbum	1
Phrurolithus festivus	2 11
Pirata hygrophylus	14569
Pisaura mirabilis	1-10 12
Pocadicnemis juncea	46
Porrhomma pygmaeum	147
" microphthalmum	4
Robertus lividus	1
Salticus scenicus	14 10 11
Segestria senoculata	39
Silometopus reussi	11
Stintula corniger	3
Sitticus pubescens	4
Steatoda bipunctata	47
Stemonyphantes lineatus	4 11
Tallusia experta	6
Tegenaria agrestis	11
" duellica	4
" gigantea	3
Tetragantha montana	45
" obtusa	1
Tibellus oblongus	1346
Theridion bimaculatum	14 11
" impressum	4
" mystaceum	4
" pallens	12567
" sisyphium	13467
" tinctum	6 10
" varians	1
Thyreosthenius parasiticus	4
Trochosa terricola	2
Xysticus cristatus	4 10 11
" ulmi	14
Walkenaeria acuminata	14
" cuspidata	59
" unicornis	49 11
Zora spinimana	1346 11
Zygella x-notata	10

Mites

Eriophyes laevis inangulis	gall on alder		34
" leisoma	"	lime	46 10
" macrorhynchus	"	maple	349
" marginatus	"	willow	234 10
" similis	"	blackthorn	3469 12